The Amazing Seeds

An assortment of flower seeds

The Amazing Seeds

ROSS E. HUTCHINS

Photographs by the author

DODD, MEAD & COMPANY · NEW YORK

To LUCILLE AND BRUCE, lovers of the out-of-doors, who also discovered the wonders of seeds.

Poem, "On a Seed," by Georgie Starbuck Galbraith, © 1960 by The New York Times Company. Reprinted by permission.

Introduction

Seeds are both the end and the beginning. A typical plant originates from the sprouting of a seed, but all a plant's life processes are aimed at the production of new seeds to continue its kind on down through time. Most of us take seeds for granted, little realizing what wonderful things they really are. Seeds are packages of life enclosed in hard, protective coats that enable them to withstand the effects of time, weather and travel.

Time in its passing has but little effect on many seeds; they may remain alive and capable of germination for hundreds or, possibly, thousands of years. The seeds of some desert plants have built-in rain gauges and will only germinate after certain amounts of rain have fallen. Other seeds have built-in time clocks or calendars that determine when they will come to life and start the production of new plants. A number of seeds are so sensitive to light that their germination is influenced by moonlight. In some seeds a one-second exposure to bright light will stimulate their germination and they can also "remember" their exposure to light and germinate at a later time.

Seeds in the form of grains have fed mankind down through the centuries. The nutritious foods stored within the seed coats are the staff of life to modern man just as they were to the ancient cliff dwellers of our Southwest and to the peoples who dwelled beside the Nile. Wheat, rice and history are closely tied together.

Plants are anchored to the ground and cannot travel, but many plants produce seeds especially fitted for transportation by air, water or on the bodies of birds and animals. Ocean currents carry sea beans to all the lands of the world and parachute-equipped seeds float on winds from continent to continent. A number of plants have mechanical devices by which they toss or shoot their seeds away. Some seeds sail on wings.

On the pages that follow are told the stories of seeds and the remarkable ways in which they are fitted to fulfill their destinies.

—R. E. H.

Contents

7

ON A SEED

This was the goal of the leaf and the root.
For this did the blossom burn its hour.
This little grain is the ultimate fruit.
This is the awesome vessel of power.

For this is the source of the root and the bud . . .
World unto world unto world remolded.
This is the seed, compact of God,
Wherein all mystery is enfolded.

GEORGIE STARBUCK GALBRAITH

The sea was the ancient cradle of life where the first primitive plants originated. They were alga-like and reproduced by spores instead of seeds. This is Sargassum weed, an alga that still lives in the sea.

Among the early land plants were the liverworts. Then, as now, their spores were produced in capsules borne at the ends of stalks.

CHAPTER 1

A World Without Seeds

Seeds are a relatively new "invention" when the total history of plant life is considered. The first primitive plants are believed to have originated in the sea about a billion years ago, but 800 million years passed before seeds came into vogue.

When simple plant life first appeared in the ancient seas, plants of that day reproduced themselves by spores, which bore no resemblance to seeds except that they were the reproductive parts of the plants' life cycles. Gradually, these simple plant forms increased in complexity, and at long last—after another hundred million years—plants became established upon the land. But millions of more years were to pass before Mother Nature got around to "inventing" a seed.

RISE OF THE MOSSES AND HORSETAILS

Just what the first green plants were like we do not know, but it is probable that they were primitive mosses and liverworts that reproduced by means of spores. The ancient *lycopod* mosses grew to huge size, some of them a hundred feet tall. Other primitive plants were hornworts and *psilotums*, both of small size and growing in damp, moist places. The *psilophytes*, tiny branching plants with no leaves or true roots, bore their spores in capsules or sporangia.

Horsetails, or *Equisetums*, were a conspicuous feature of that

Moss capsules, left, open when mature and liberate the spores which are carried away in the wind. At right, modern horsetails, or Equisetums, *plants that appeared about 350 million years ago.*

long-ago landscape, too. Some were as large as our largest trees today, yet they had no seeds either and reproduced by spores.

THE COMING OF THE FERNS

The most advanced of the spore-bearing plants of the ancient world of millions of years ago were the ferns. They, too, grew to great size. These were the times of giant plants and, somewhat later, of giant animals such as the dinosaurs. Our modern ferns, though much smaller, look very like the fossilized remains of the ancient ferns and reproduction is like that of their ancestors, from spores and not seeds.

The spore sacs of ferns are usually formed on the undersides of the fronds, but in some species there are special, spore-bearing stalks. These spore cases are called *sori* and the spores, like those of mosses, require very damp, wet conditions for growth.

From the ferns came the seed ferns, plants that were fernlike but which bore *ovules* that became seeds. And the ferns developed quite differently from the mosses and plants that came before them. The story of seeds can be said to start with the seed ferns.

A moss plant begins life when a spore germinates on damp soil, producing an alga-like network. From this eventually arises the typical leafy moss plant that grows to be several inches tall. This is the *gametophyte* or sexual part of the moss's life cycle and, when the moss plant is mature, male and female organs are produced at the tip. Fertilization occurs when raindrops or dew enable the male cells to swim or be splashed to the female cells. When this occurs, a stalk bearing a spore capsule at its tip grows up out of the leafy plant. This is the *sporophyte* or spore-bearing part of its life history. Spores produced in the capsule blow away and start other moss plants.

In the life cycle of a fern, which is a step higher on the evolutionary ladder, we find that the gametophyte, or sexual part

Ferns growing on the bark of a tree, left, are sporophytes *or the spore-bearing portion of the life cycle. Right, a fern that lived millions of years ago. Its fossilized remains look much like a modern fern frond.*

Fern spores are produced in sori *or spore cases on the leaves (as shown here) or upon special, spore-bearing stalks.*

of the plant, is reduced to a flat, heart-shaped little structure growing upon damp soil. When mature, this gametophyte produces male and female cells on its under surface and fertilization occurs when male cells swim to the female cells during periods of rainfall. From this fertilized cell there eventually grows the typical, leafy fern plant having true roots. This is the sporophyte part of the fern's cycle.

SEEDS ARRIVE

Thus, we see that while the green, leafy stage of the moss is the gametophyte, the green leafy stage of the fern is the sporophyte. As plants climbed up the evolutionary ladder, the sporophyte stage gradually became more and more important, while the gametophyte stage was gradually reduced in size and importance. When true seed plants came into vogue, the gametophytes were further reduced in size and enclosed in hard, protective seed coats, while the sporophytes became the main portions of the plants. The old-fashioned spore-bearing plants

The main portion of the primitive hornwort is the flat gameto-phyte, while the spore-bearing stalk is the sporophyte.

continued on down through time but little changed, while the seed plants increased in abundance and diversity and eventually covered the earth.

The first seeds were "naked seeds"; that is, they had no thick, protective coats as do most modern seeds. But they were many-

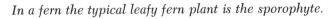

In a fern the typical leafy fern plant is the sporophyte.

celled and contained embryos or young plants. Such plants were no longer dependent upon rains for fertilization as had been the case with the spore-bearing ferns and mosses. Pollen, or male cells, were carried to a female plant by means of winds or insects. This was pollination as we know it today.

During the days of the dinosaurs the naked-seed plants flourished and great forests came into being. The ancestors of our redwoods and pines and other great conifers grew to tremendous size, and there were other naked-seed plants and trees, such as spruces, firs, ginkgos, and the palmlike cycads. In time, the seed ferns disappeared, and yet the true flowering plants with their covered seeds were still in the future.

AN UNSOLVED MYSTERY

One of the mysteries of botany is the way in which covered-seed plants evolved from naked-seed plants. So far, no fossils of intermediate plants have been found. We know that there must have been a gradual change from one type to the other, but what these in-between plants were like is unknown. They are missing links in the chain of plant life.

We do know that by about 150 million years ago such cov-

Like their relatives, the pines, cedars are naked-seed plants. Shown here is an open cone of a cedar with several seeds.

The mallows trace their ancestry back to the days of the ancient flowering plants. Shown here is a cotton bloom, a modern mallow.

ered-seed plants as magnolias, buttercups, and mallows were already present, since fossils of their leaves, stems, and floral parts have been found. Such plants are called *angiosperms,* a term of Greek origin meaning "seeds enclosed in envelopes." All our present-day flowering plants are angiosperms.

Plants developed in great variety, and their seeds are of endless form, coloration, and size. Those in the present world range in size from minute tobacco and orchid seeds to the huge double coconut or coco-de-mer which often weighs up to sixty pounds and is the world's largest seed. Some seeds are equipped with wings or parachutes that enable them to sail through the air. Others bear hooked spines by which they attach themselves to animals for transportation, and still others are enclosed in edible fruits that are apt to be carried away and dropped by animals where they will grow.

The world's seeds were not created overnight. Their story stretches far back into the dim mists of time. And if there are a few unsolved mysteries along the way, there are also marvelous miracles in the ways that Mother Nature has arranged for plants to reproduce themselves.

Close-up of lily anthers showing adhering pollen grains

This is the attractive bloom of the passion flower. Note the five stamens and three-lobed stigma. It is pollinated by bees that rub pollen off the anthers onto their backs as they seek nectar at the flower's center.

CHAPTER 2

A Seed Is Formed

$\mathcal{E}$ach spring among the plants, as for millions of years, the complicated processes that end with the formation of new seeds begin. The flowers that bloom in the spring or summer have but one great purpose, the production of seeds to continue the species. These parcels of life are the links in the chain that enable most plants to continue from generation to generation. The flowers produced by plants are of infinite form and structure; no two kinds are ever exactly alike. They vary from the simple blooms of grasses to the gorgeous blooms of orchids, and from our tiny bluets to the great *Rafflesias* of Oriental lands which may be a yard across. But whatever the forms of flowers, their primary purpose is to secure the transfer of pollen from one to the other to bring about fertilization and the production of seeds.

The pollination of a flower is the first step in the chain of events that leads eventually to the formation of the seeds. Without pollination there can be no seeds. In order to understand how seeds are formed we should know something about the structure of the female part of the flower. If you will examine a tulip, for example, you will notice that, extending up from the center, is a column-like structure with a knobbed head. This is the *pistil*. The top or enlarged head of the pistil is called the *stigma* and it is upon the stigma that pollen must be deposited during pollination. Below the stigma is a necklike portion or

19

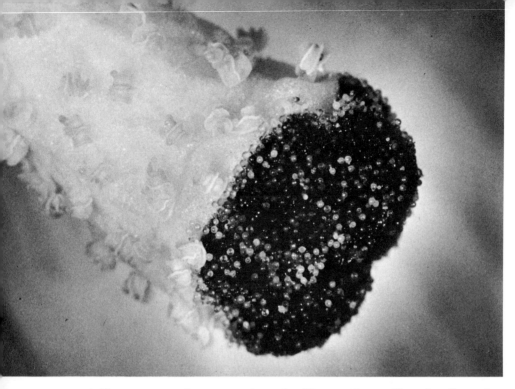

Pollen grains on the stigma of an okra bloom. They will send pollen tubes down through the pistil to the ovary where young seeds will be fertilized.

style. Below the style is the expanded, bulb-shaped *ovary*. If the ovary is carefully cut open it will be found to be divided into three chambers, each with tiny, developing *ovules* or young seeds. All the members of the lily and related families have three-chambered ovaries but flowers of other types have from one to many chambers.

FLOWER POLLINATION

The dustlike pollen grains which we see on the anthers of flowers are the male reproductive cells which, in order to bring about fertilization, must be deposited upon the pistils or female organs of a flower. This is the process we know as pollination.

The surface of the female stigma, where pollen is deposited, is usually moist and sticky so that the grains readily adhere to it. Once lodged upon the stigma, the pollen grains absorb moisture and other substances and begin to swell. Soon pollen tubes push out and begin growing down through the necklike style; as they

Extreme close-up of corn pollen grains adhering to a silk (stigma). When germinated they send pollen tubes down through the long silk to the ovule.

One corn silk is attached to each developing ovule on the ear. Should any of the silks be destroyed, the ovules to which they are attached will fail to develop.

increase in length they are nourished by the tissues of the stigma and guided on their way downward toward the ovary. Their growth is quite rapid in most flowers, but in some cases the pollen tubes may stop growth for several months while the ovules are developing. The distance the pollen tube has to travel depends upon the length of the style or the distance from the stigma to the ovary. In some flowers this distance may be only a fraction of an inch, but in the case of corn the silks, which are actually the styles, may reach twenty inches in length. The strands of corn silk extend into the ear where one is attached to each of the developing ovules or grains of corn. If you will carefully unwrap a young ear the silken strands can be traced to their attachments, one to each of the ovules.

In a typical flower the ovules are attached to the inner wall of the ovary by short stalks. At one end of each ovule there are tiny openings called *micropyles* (meaning "little doors") and it is through these that the pollen tubes enter. When the pollen tubes reach the ovary they follow along the inner wall and one tube enters the micropyle of each ovule. Within the ovule, the male chromosomes of the pollen tube fuse with the female chromosomes, combining their genetic contents. These chromosomes are what determine all the characteristics of the future plant. They are like microscopic blueprints, containing within themselves every detail of the plant that will grow from the mature seed: the form of its leaves, the shape and color of its blooms, and all its other characteristics. In the process of fertilization or union of the chromosomes there is a blending of the genetic characters of the male and female cells. Since one pollen grain germinates into one pollen tube that penetrates down through the style to fertilize one ovule, it is obvious that if an ovary contains a hundred ovules, at least a hundred pollen grains must be deposited upon the stigma. It is probable that not all of these pollen grains came from the same male plant or male part of another flower. Thus, it is also probable that the plants that

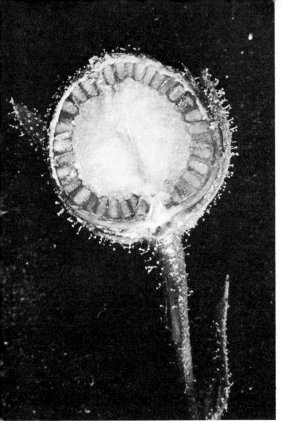

Left, developing ovules of moth mullein cut in cross-section. Right, nearly mature pansy seeds in a pod which will later split to liberate them.

grow from the seeds in a pod will show considerable variation in individual characteristics. Some of these may be better adapted to the local soil and climatic conditions than others and this, of course, is advantageous to the survival of the species.

DEVELOPMENT OF THE OVULE

After fertilization has taken place and the tiny ovules have begun to grow into seeds, the walls of the ovary, too, begin growth. All this growth requires much food and such things as sugars, proteins and fatty materials begin flowing into the ovary from the stems and leaves. Most of these foods have been manufactured in the leaves which the plant holds up to the sunlight to absorb its energy. This sun energy is used by the green chlorophyll in its important work of food manufacture. When flowing into the ovary the foods must of necessity be in liquid form but, once they have reached their destination, they are changed into insoluble starches, fats and other materials.

While the ovary itself serves, at first, merely as a storage place or seed pod for the developing seeds, it later, in many instances, takes on other duties or functions. In the case of the pansy, for example, the ovary merely splits open upon maturity and liberates the seeds it contains. In numerous other cases, however, the walls of the seed pod become thickened or become covered with hooks, spines or wings to help distribute the seed or seeds it contains. This is what happens in the case of beggar's lice, maple, cocklebur and many other plants. In numerous other cases the ovaries develop into interesting mechanical devices which toss seeds away from the parent plant to make sure that they will not fall to the ground beneath the parent and grow into a crowded cluster of young plants. A good example is the wild geranium which has springlike devices to propel its seeds several feet through the air.

The ovaries of many plants, on the other hand, develop into fleshy fruits but not all fleshy fruits are derived from enlarged ovaries. Actually, there is considerable variation in the origin of various fruits and fruit parts and botanists classify many things as fruits that you or I might not consider as such. They are considered to be fruits because they are matured ovaries. As a result, tomatoes, cucumbers, snap beans, peppers, squashes, buckwheat, corn and many nuts are classified as fruit even though this term may not seem correct to us. However, not all fruits are derived entirely from ovaries; in many cases what we consider to be the fruit developed from petals, stamens, and sepals (the green, leafy structures beneath the petals). Examples of such fruits are apples and strawberries. In some cases, too, what we usually consider to be the hard seed coat is actually developed from the inner wall of the ovary and is, technically, not a part of the seed at all. The hard "pits" of plums, peaches, cherries and apricots are not really seeds; the true seeds are enclosed within them and are covered with only thin walls.

Crotalaria, *a member of the pea family, has its ovules enclosed in a pod.
The pod develops from the walls of the ovary.*

This cut-away view of a lotus ovary shows the developing ovules.

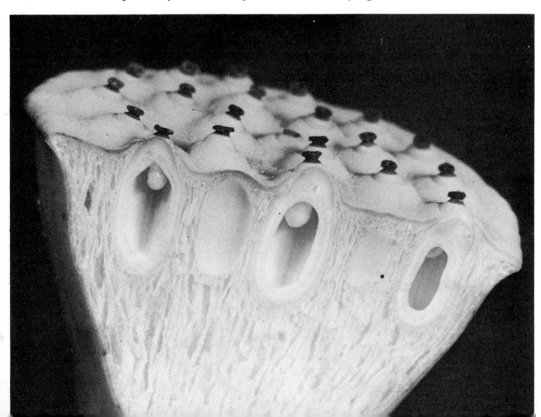

A package of garden or flower seeds can be purchased for a few cents, but its contents consist of marvelous things. From the dry seeds may eventually grow edible vegetables or beautiful flowers. The plants that grow from the seeds may be millions of times larger than the seeds themselves. It has been estimated that the tobacco plant that grows from a seed—one of the smallest seeds—may weigh up to 20 million times the weight of the original seed! Actually, there is no relationship between the sizes of seeds and the plants that grow from them. A coconut is five or six inches in diameter and grows into a tree less than a hundred feet tall and not much over a foot in diameter, while a redwood seed, no larger than a milkweed seed, may grow into a giant tree three hundred feet tall and, perhaps, thirty feet in diameter and containing enough wood to build an entire housing subdivision. In general, however, the larger a seed is and the more stored food it contains, the better are its chances of successful growth into a plant.

The outside coat of a seed is called the *testa* and, in many seeds, it is extremely hard and flinty. Its purpose, of course, is to protect the inner contents and it does this so effectively that some seeds, such as those of the lotus, may remain alive for hundreds of years.

A package of mixed flower seeds contains remarkable things. Each seed holds an embryonic plant and a store of food to start it out in life.

Close-up of the seeds in a flower seed mixture

The seed coats of many seeds, instead of being smooth, are marked and colored in many ways. Perhaps the most ornamental of all seeds are coral beans (*Abrus*) produced by a climbing vine growing in various tropical countries including Florida. One end of the bean is glossy black and the other end is bright scarlet. They are very attractive, but are also very poisonous. The seeds of many common plants have surface sculpturings or are covered with spines or pits. Some are of strange shapes. A package of mixed flower seeds, if examined under a hand lens, will reveal some surprising and interesting examples.

27

While the outside of a seed is interesting, the truly amazing part of the seed is hidden inside. Within the seed is contained an embryonic plant, stored away in a convenient package ready to grow into a new plant when conditions are favorable. A seed may look dead but it is actually a living plant whose life processes have been slowed down almost to the stopping point.

Enclosed within the testa or seed coat of a typical angiosperm or flowering plant are either one or two food-storage parts or *cotyledons*. This stored food is called *endosperm*. In the case of a bean, for example, there are two cotyledons which separate when the bean is split open. These are actually seed-leaves in which food is stored. Between the cotyledons may be seen the pale, embryonic bean plant consisting of the *plumule* which will grow upward and become the stalk and the *hypocotyl* which will become the root. In the case of the bean, the embryonic plant is quite small, but in the castor bean the embryonic leaf completely fills the space between the two cotyledons. When the seed germinates, the cotyledons push upward; in some cases they do not reach the light, but in the bean they are pushed upward above the soil and turn green. For awhile the cotyledons help manufacture food; then, when their contained store of food is exhausted, they shrivel and die. In the meantime, true leaves develop to carry on the work of food manufacture. In corn, wheat and other members of the grass family there is only one cotyledon, but food is not stored here. In this case the food or endosperm is not absorbed by the plant until the seed sprouts. Stored food materials consist of starch, sugar, oil and protein which nourish the young plant until it has developed green leaves and a root system. After the store of seed food has been all used up the young plant is on its own.

Thus, a seed is a package of plant life conveniently enclosed in a tough shell that protects it against drying, temperature, and the effects of time. Within its walls are contained all the things

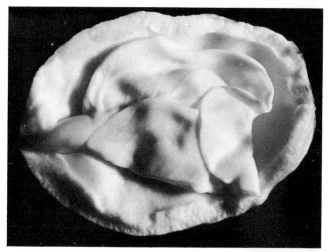

A common bean split in two shows the two halves or cotyledons and, between them, a pale embryonic bean plant. One part will become the root, the other the stem and leaves.

A castor bean is similar, but the pale embryonic leaf is larger and fills the space between the cotyledons. At this stage there is no chlorophyll in the leaf.

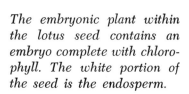

The embryonic plant within the lotus seed contains an embryo complete with chlorophyll. The white portion of the seed is the endosperm.

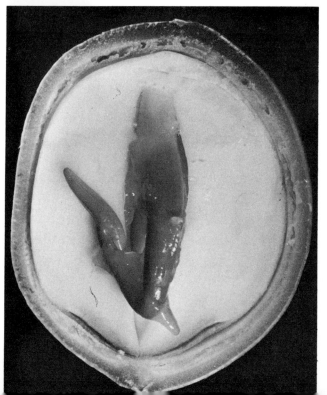

needed to launch a new plant on its career. Seeds are among the most marvelous things in all nature.

MONOCOTS AND DICOTS

The flowering plant world is divided into two great tribes; these consist of those whose seeds contain two parts or cotyledons and of those whose seeds have but one cotyledon. Those with two-parted seeds are called *dicots*, while those with but one cotyledon are called *monocots*.

Common examples of monocot plants are grasses, lilies, orchids, palms and bananas. In the case of corn, the white, starchy end of the grain is the endosperm. A large part of the world's food supply is furnished by food materials stored in monocot seeds. For many centuries, grains such as wheat, rye, rice, barley and oats have been the "staff of life" to human civilizations. Corn, a New World plant, was added to man's sources of food when he crossed the Atlantic. Monocot seed plants are also characterized by having parallel veined leaves and flower parts in threes or multiples of three. This can easily be seen in many lilies; the ovary is three-celled and the stigma often has three divisions. There are usually six stamens. There are about 50,000 kinds or species of plants of this type. While many monocots

This lily is a typical monocot, with six anthers and a three-lobed stigma.

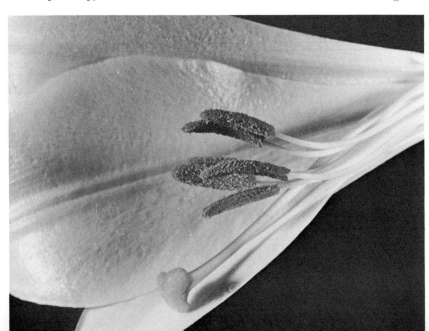

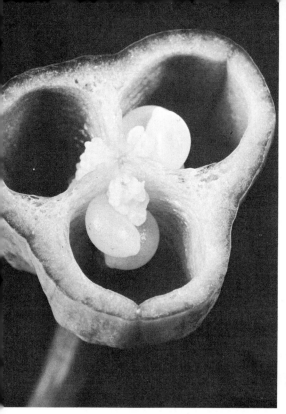

The jonquil seed pod, left, has three chambers, typical of monocots. The poppy bloom, is a dicot, with many stamens and a many-lobed stigma.

such as grasses, cattails and palms have very inconspicuous flowers, many of our most beautiful blooms are produced by monocot plants.

The dicot plants, on the other hand, have net-veined leaves. Their flower parts are in multiples of four or five. To this plant tribe belong most of the world's most important and abundant plants. There are about 200,000 kinds, including the willows, oaks, elms, buttercups, apples, peaches, roses, sunflowers and others.

REPRODUCTION WITHOUT SEEDS

Nature seldom puts all her eggs in one basket. While seeds are the normal method of propagation of most modern plants, there are many kinds that also multiply by means of tubers, bulbs, runners, rhizomes (rootlike structures), and other devices.

31

Commercially, bananas are not usually produced from seeds. "Suckers" from the plant are set out to start new plants.

In some cases seed production has been eliminated entirely. To grow Irish potatoes, a farmer does not plant seeds; he plants tubers that have been cut up so that each portion contains an "eye" from which a potato plant will grow. In the case of sugar cane, stalks are buried and new canes arise from each joint. Many trees, such as silver poplars, grow from roots extending out from a "parent" tree. Strawberry plants put out runners that take root and produce new plants. In the case of *Bryophyllum*, the leaves produce plantlets at their notches and these fall to the ground and take root.

This kind of vegetative reproduction is the rule in many of our most important plants—banana, citrus fruits, date, pineapple, apple, pear, peach and pecan. Many wild plants, too, use this system. Examples are mint, many grasses, poison ivy, sweet flag, cattail and some ferns.

To the farmer and flower grower vegetative reproduction has the advantage that desirable traits in plants are retained, that is, they "come true." In plants growing from seeds there may be a

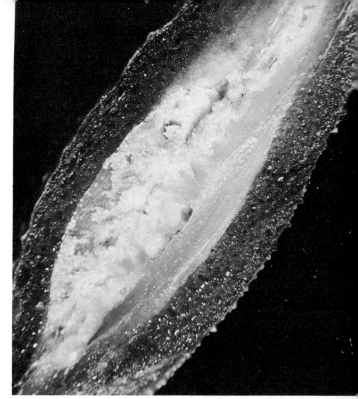

This is an immature orchid seed pod containing the tiny seeds. There are nearly a million orchid seeds to the ounce.

blending of characteristics from two or more parents. Also, vegetative production of new plants is usually faster. Many of our most important flowers are normally produced vegetatively. A few examples are roses, carnations, poinsettias, gladioli, hyacinths, iris, and dahlias.

HOW BIG, HOW SMALL

There is tremendous variation in both size and weight of seeds. The tiny seeds of willows float in the air, buoyed up by their attached bits of down. The seeds of dandelions and sow thistles have parachutes which enable breezes to carry them long distances. The largest seeds in the world are those of a palm that grows in the interior valleys of the Seychelles Islands in the Indian Ocean. These seeds are called coco-de-mer, "nuts of the sea," and weigh up to sixty pounds each. These seeds look like double coconuts and are often carried by ocean currents to distant shores.

Probably the smallest of all seeds are those of epiphytic or-

33

All these seeds come from this one poppy capsule. Poppy seeds are very small, there being 140,000 to the ounce.

chids that resemble dust and can be blown by wind or stick to birds' feet and be transported to the bark of distant trees where germination occurs. Due to their minute size and the small amount of stored food they contain, their germination is very difficult. Another of the world's smallest seeds is that of tobacco. In an ounce there are about 400,000 seeds. A single tobacco seed

Beans are among the larger seeds, with only about 100 to the ounce.

weighs only 0.0902 milligram (a milligram is one-thousandth of a gram). Among the smallest of seeds are those of witchweed, a plant that grows as a parasite on corn and is a serious pest since it attaches its roots to those of corn and saps out their nourishment. Each witchweed plant produces about half a million microscopic seeds, each one measuring only 0.0078 inch long. These seeds, in spite of their small size, may lie dormant in the soil for up to twenty years before germinating. They will not germinate until they come in contact with the roots of their host plants. The witchweed itself bears a rather attractive red flower. In fact, in South Africa, it is called *rooibloemtjie*, meaning "little red flower." It is probable that, next to some tropical orchid seeds, the seeds of Kalanchoe are the smallest. These are succulent herbs often grown as houseplants. Most of them are native to South Africa.

As a means of comparing the sizes of some common seeds, we might consider the relative numbers per ounce. They are as follows:

SEEDS	NO. SEEDS PER OUNCE
Lima bean	25-75
Watermelon	200-300
Cucumber	1,100
Radish	2,000-4,000
Onion	9,500
Columbine	15,500
Lettuce	25,000
Celery	72,000
Alyssum	90,000
Coleus	100,000
English daisy	135,000
Poppy	140,000
Foxglove	180,000
Petunia	285,000
Tobacco	400,000
Linaria	600,000
Begonia	1,000,000
Kalanchoe	2,500,000

*A milkweed seed (cen-
ter) with seeds of Big
Tree Sequoia, the
world's largest tree.*

The sizes and shapes of seeds are of infinite variety. Shown opposite are shadowgrams of forty-seven different seeds, all natural size. Below is the key to their identification.

KEY TO SHADOWGRAMS

1. Sunflower
2. Bean
3. Lotus
4. Acorn (oak)
5. Dutchman's pipe
6. Yucca
7. Watermelon
8. Big Tree Sequoia
9. Franseria
10. Honesty (*Lunaria*)
11. Sandspur
12. Milkweed
13. Magnolia
14. Spanish needle
15. Needle grass (*Stipa*)
16. Sweet cicely

17. Goat's-beard
18. Wild rice
19. Zinnia
20. Clematis
21. Maple
22. Apple
23. Mimosa
24. Flax
25. Catalpa
26. Datura
27. Four-o'clock
28. Calendula
29. Redbud
30. Maypop
31. Witch hazel
32. Spurge nettle

33. Gaillardia
34. Wheat
35. Cornflower
36. Wild carrot
37. Crotalaria
38. Cleome
39. Larkspur
40. Thistle
41. Partridge pea
42. Lettuce
43. Black-eyed Susan
44. Verbena
45. Mullein
46. Poppy
47. Petunia

*These are shadowgrams of forty-seven different seeds, all natural size.
See key on the opposite page for identification.*

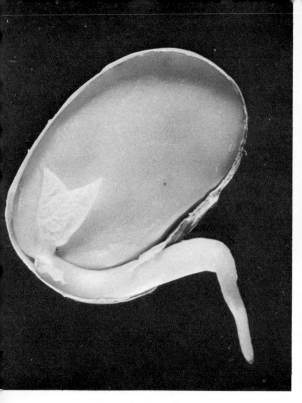

A sprouting bean, left, is split in two, showing one cotyledon (food storage section), the developing leaves, and the root which has already emerged from the seed. Right, the stalk of the bean has emerged from the soil carrying with it the cotyledons (seed leaves) and first true leaves.

Below, the stalk has increased in length. True leaves emerge between the cotyledons which dry up and fall off when their food store is exhausted.

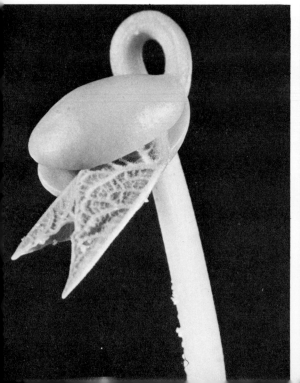

CHAPTER 3

Germination of the Seed

When a seed is mature and falls away from the parent plant it is a finished product. Within its walls are contained all the things it will require to start a new plant out on its own. A bean, for example, contains two cotyledons filled with food stores and a complete embryonic plant. When the bean is planted, it at once begins absorbing moisture from the surrounding soil. This moisture penetrates the seed coat and is absorbed by the cotyledons. The life processes that have lain dormant, perhaps for many years, within the embryo begin "ticking." The seed is again a living, breathing bit of plant life.

Ever so slowly the cotyledons expand, breaking open the hard seed coat. The root thrusts out, anchors itself in the soil, and begins producing fine root hairs that rapidly absorb moisture from the surrounding soil particles. The plumule, too, grows and expands and pushes upward through the soil. The force of gravity determines the direction each will follow. The root follows the pull of gravity and grows downward, while the plumule resists the pull and grows upward. Food materials stored within the cotyledons begin flowing into the growing plantlet to nourish it. Each part has its role in bringing a new plant into being.

WATER

Life originated in the water and water is necessary to all living

When seeds absorb water they swell and exert enormous pressures. Here, the glass flask was broken.

things. Cells of a living plant contain from 70 to 90 per cent water and are, thus, more water than anything else.

While ovules or young seeds are growing they contain large amounts of moisture, which is lost as the seeds mature. By the time the seeds are ready to be shed they may contain as little as 4 per cent water. A dry seed is dormant and will remain so until more moisture is absorbed. In general, dry seeds will remain alive much longer than damp seeds and the longer seeds are stored, the more moisture they lose. High temperatures also cause them to lose moisture. It is interesting, too, that different seeds react differently to water loss and absorption. When peanuts are stored they reach a moisture content of about 8 per cent, while beans stored at the same temperature reach about 16 per cent.

When seeds come into contact with water they begin absorbing it through their coats in relatively large quantities. In fact, seeds often double their weights when planted in moist soil. Each kind of seed must absorb a rather definite amount of water before it will germinate. Corn must contain about 40 per cent and beans about 70 per cent water for germination to begin.

The physical forces that cause seeds to absorb water often exert enormous pressures. Water entering dry seeds operates against a force of several hundred pounds per square inch. This can be demonstrated by filling a bottle with dry beans and then covering them with water. The beans will absorb moisture and swell, exerting sufficient pressure to break the bottle.

SEEDS AND GRAVITY

Most of us are familiar with the old story of the inexperienced farmer who carefully planted each grain of corn so that the stems would grow up and the roots would grow down. While it might seem reasonable that seeds should be planted so that the shoots and roots would be pointed in the proper direction, the truth is that it makes no difference at all how a seed is planted. If a bean is planted on its "back" the stem will curve upward and the root will bend downward. But we might ask, how do roots and stems "know" which way to go?

As beans germinate and push upward they have sufficient force to lift quite heavy weights. In this case the lid of the dish was lifted.

Regardless of the position in which seeds are planted, the roots always grow downward. These beans were planted in three positions yet all roots turned down.

These three grains of corn were planted upsidedown, sidewise, and rightside up, yet the roots grew downward and the stalks upward.

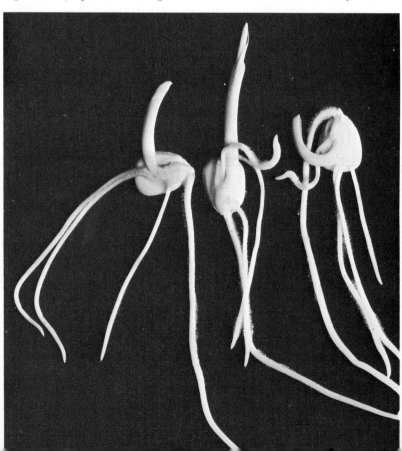

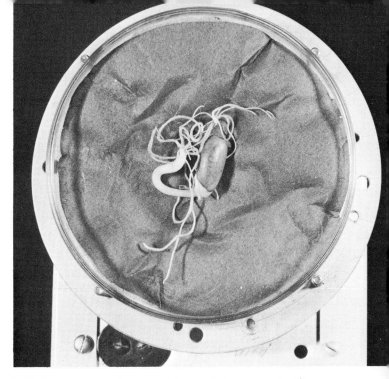

This bean sprouted in a dish revolving once in 24 hours. The roots attempted to grow downward but were confused by the rotation of the dish.

Research by botanists has shed some light on this question, but not all the answers are known. A plant's response to gravity is called *geotropism* and this may be either positive or negative. The bending of roots and stems in relation to the pull of gravity is caused by the presence of chemical growth regulators or *auxins,* secreted by the plant. When a stem is placed on its side the auxins tend to flow downward so that they stimulate growth on the lower side. This causes the stem to bend or grow upward. In the case of a root, the cells are more sensitive to the auxins and their growth is actually slowed down by them. Now when a root is placed in horizontal position the auxins flow to its lower side as was the case with stems. In the case of roots, however, the auxins inhibit, or slow down growth, so that the root bends downward through the soil. In other words, auxins stimulate growth when they are present in small amounts but slow down growth when they are present in large amounts or when cells are especially sensitive to them. It is only the actively growing tips of roots that respond to the force of gravity. When the tips of roots are cut off they do not bend downward.

It is thus that stems and roots "know" which way to grow.

The more we learn about the wonder of growing things the more we realize how well they are fitted for the lives they live. If seeds fall from a plant in summer and immediately sprout and begin growth, there is a good chance that winter will arrive before they can mature and produce a new crop of seeds. Some plants, of course, are adapted to do this; the seeds produce plants in late summer that begin growth by putting out a few leaves and a root and, with the coming of the following spring, the plant resumes growth. On the other hand, such seeds as those of cottonwood and willow remain alive for only a few days and, if they do not alight upon moist soil where they can germinate immediately, they will die.

As a general rule, the seeds of most wild plants do not all germinate at once or, sometimes, not even the next summer; their germination may be spread over several years. This is a great advantage since periods of drought or abnormal cold might wipe out all the young plants if the seeds all germinated at once. In the common cocklebur each bur contains two seeds, known as the upper and lower seeds, one larger than the other. The lower, or largest seed in each bur, germinates the next spring after maturing, while the upper seed does not germinate until the second spring. This arrangement doubles the chance that the seeds will encounter favorable growing conditions. It is believed that the difference in germination time is governed by the thickness of seed coats, which apparently controls the absorption of oxygen. In the case of the upper seed, the coat must decay away before it can absorb sufficient oxygen for germination.

Cockleburs, like many other plants, are limited in their geographic range by the length of time required for seeds to be

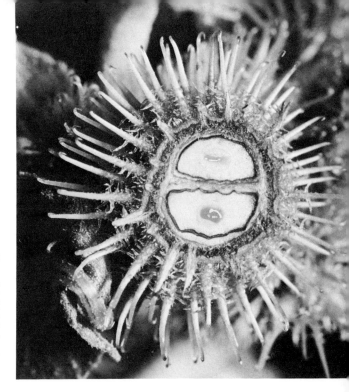

Close-up of a cocklebur cut open to show the two seeds. The smaller upper seed will germinate the second spring while the lower seed will germinate the first spring after the seeds are formed.

produced. Within the United States, cockleburs have a long enough growing season in most areas to produce mature seeds, but in Canada, where summers are short, cocklebur plants do not have enough time to produce seeds before frost. Thus, these plants do not occur in Canada.

A TIME TO SPROUT

Many seeds will not grow immediately after falling from the parent plant; they require a period of after-ripening. As a matter of fact, this is a characteristic of most wild plants native to our temperate climate. Silver maples shed their seeds in late summer but will not germinate until the next spring. Many domesticated plants, too, must undergo a period of rest before germination. In the case of barley, about one-fourth of the seeds will germinate at once, but after a month they will all germinate. This is another case where Nature takes the precaution to see that all the young plants will not perish if all of them grow at once and they encounter a period of unfavorable weather. Petunia and portulaca seeds that mature in early summer will

45

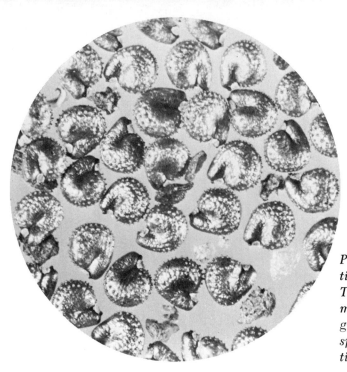

Portulaca seeds are very tiny, with a metallic sheen. They mature in early summer but do not sprout and grow until the following spring. They have built-in timing mechanisms.

not germinate until the following spring. Portulaca seeds, like those of many other plants, have a long life. In one test, over 90 per cent of these seeds germinated after storage for 20 years, and a few germinated after 40 years!

Some seeds must be subjected to cold before they will germinate. Thus, it is said that cold weather "breaks" their dormancy. This, of course, is an adaptation of cold climate seeds to prevent germination until the ensuing spring. Some seeds must be stored at low temperature under moist conditions to "break" their dormancy while others require storage in dry conditions. Immediately after harvest, lettuce seeds will not usually germinate at all, but after sixteen weeks of dry storage at 86 degrees Fahrenheit they all germinated. Seeds of some wild plants require an after-ripening period of several years.

In order to prevent germination of their seeds, many fruits contain chemical inhibitors that do not allow their seeds to germinate. It would be fatal to a tomato seed if it germinated within the ripe fruit. Thus, the fruit contains a chemical substance that

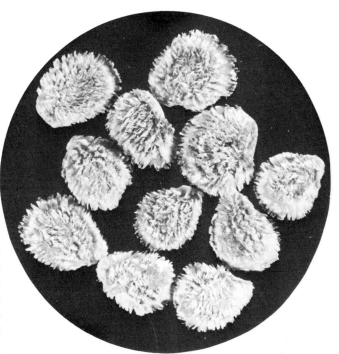

Tomato seeds are covered with "fur." Tomatoes, like most other fruits, contain a substance that prevents the germination of their seeds while they are still contained within the fruit.

prevents germination as long as the seeds are contained within it. Other seeds have germination-inhibiting substances in them that must be soaked out before they can germinate. Such substances have been found in the seeds of many desert plants that must experience considerable rain before they will germinate. If these seeds germinated during a short, wet period they could not survive. It is only when long periods of rain occur that they germinate. Thus, in effect, they have built-in rain gauges.

SEEDS AND LIGHT

There is an old belief that certain seeds must be planted in the dark of the moon and others in the light of the moon. While most modern botanists and horticulturists place no faith in this belief, there are indications that many seeds are sensitive to light rays. While it is probable that the phases of the moon have little effect on seed germination, it has actually been found that tobacco seeds are so sensitive to light that moonlight stimulates their germination.

47

Lettuce seeds, very sensitive to light, will not germinate in total darkness.

Seeds of Nigella do not germinate well in light; they must have darkness.

It is known, of course, that the flowering of many plants is governed by the length of the days. Those plants that bloom in spring or autumn are known as "short-day" plants while those that bloom in midsummer are known as "long-day" plants. Blooming of these plants is controlled by certain growth-regulating substances and it has been found that it is actually the length of the nights, rather than the days, that influences them.

Some seeds require light for germination, some are not affected, while to others, light slows down or actually prevents germination. Light speeds up the germination of such seeds as those of mistletoe, evening primrose, willow-herb, loosestrife and many grasses, yet many mistletoe seeds will not germinate at all in darkness. On the other hand, beans, corn, clover and most small grains will germinate equally well in either light or darkness. The light-sensitivity of many seeds is so great that one second of exposure will trigger their germination. But light

Some plants, such as beans, appear to grow faster in darkness than in light, but this is due to rapid cell elongation and not to true growth. The bean shown at the right was grown in darkness.

also prevents the germination of *Phacelia, Nigella* (love-in-the-mist), several kinds of lilies and many other plants. Recent research shows that seeds, like some flowers, are influenced by day length and may be classified as short-day seeds or long-day seeds. Begonia seeds germinate during long days, while catchfly (*Silene*) seeds appear to germinate best during short days.

It has been found that there is a relationship between temperature and light in the case of certain seeds. Lettuce seeds will germinate in darkness only within narrow temperature limits but, in light, they germinate regardless of temperatures. It has been found, too, that dry lettuce seeds are not sensitive to light but when moistened they become sensitive to very dim light and will then go ahead and germinate. Strangely, if lettuce seeds that have been moistened and exposed to light are dried they retain the effect of the light and will germinate in darkness. They seem to "remember" the light. It is apparently the red portion of the spectrum that influences them most. To the farmer and gardener, the light sensitivity of seeds is important. Seeds that require light for germination must not be planted too deep.

Once a seed has germinated, the plant grows for a while independent of light, or until the food supply within the seed is exhausted. It then begins to slow down and will eventually die. Of course, for a time it will appear to grow very rapidly but this is because of rapid cell elongation. Actually, no food is being manufactured in the absence of light and the "growth" is largely due to rapid water absorption.

SEEDS IN THE ATOMIC AGE

Seeds, like many other things in this Atomic Age, have had their inner workings probed by radioactive substances. Radio-isotopes are often used to trace the absorption and movement of minerals into and through seeds and growing plants. Such techniques have explained many hitherto but little understood

Cactus seeds were exposed to atomic radiation and then planted. Those at the right sprouted, grew for a time, then died. They were injured by the radiation. Some of the others may develop unusual characteristics.

things about plant life. Seeds have also been treated with radioactive substances to determine their effect upon germination. The speed and percentage of seed germination have been found to be increased in wheat, rye, barley, corn and horse chestnut when these seeds are treated with uranium compounds. Yields of common peas are increased by soaking the seeds in solutions of uranyl nitrate. Vegetable seeds were stimulated in their germination when soaked for several days in uranium solutions diluted down to one part in 10,000 parts of water. On the other hand, radium rays killed seeds when they were too close—¾ inch —to the source. As they were moved farther away, however, their germination was stimulated.

At the atomic bomb tests on Bikini Atoll in 1946, samples of corn were placed on the ships anchored in the lagoon in the target area. Later, when these seeds were planted, it was found that the plants that grew from the seeds were defective and abnormal. Whether the treatment of seeds by atomic radiation holds promise of being helpful or not remains to be seen. It has been found, however, that if seeds are irradiated with dosages

Germination of seeds with very hard coats can be speeded up by soften-ing their coats with acids or filing them down. These hard lotus seeds were sanded down on one side, after which they quickly sprouted.

ranging from 15,000 r. to 30,000 r. the plants that grow from them will show changes brought about by the effect upon their chromosomes. These changes are passed down to future off-spring, and thus this technique may make it possible to produce new plant varieties artificially.

Seeds have also been subjected to powerful electrical fields which apparently increase their internal temperatures. Alfalfa seeds treated in this way showed almost double the percentage of germination.

HINTS ON SEED GERMINATION

It is always a thrill to see apparently lifeless seeds come to life and start growing. A seed appears to be a dead thing, but when placed in proper conditions of moisture, temperature and light the dormant life within the seed coat begins to tick again and soon a new plant is formed. Most kinds of seeds will grow with no further attention, outside of watering, but scientists have learned some very helpful facts about germination.

In the case of some biennial plants, or plants that normally require two years to flower and produce seeds, it has been found that they can be made to complete their growth in one year if the seeds receive special treatment. This is done by *low temperature vernalization,* which consists of soaking the seeds in water and then holding them at temperatures just above the freezing point for several weeks. Such treatment shortens the vegetative growth stage so that the plants will complete their growth and produce seeds in one year. Winter cereals and lettuce that normally need two growing seasons to produce seeds will produce seeds in one season if they are first *vernalized.*

The seed coats of some seeds such as the hard seeds of some grasses, lotus, and many others will germinate best if their coats are scratched or filed to allow water to penetrate. Lotus seeds

Avocado seeds usually sprout if they are placed in damp sand.

germinate quite easily if one side of each one is sandpapered away until the white, inner part of the seed is visible. When placed in a jar of water the sanded seeds will sprout within a few days; otherwise only a few seeds are apt to germinate after months of submersion. In nature, hard seed coats are slowly softened by long submersion in water or by the action of molds or bacteria.

Generally speaking, it is best to sow seeds in soil that has been sterilized. This can be done by heating it in a pressure cooker for about half an hour, or you can buy a bag of sterile soil substitute such as milled sphagnum moss or vermiculite. As a further assurance that soil fungi and bacteria will not injure the tender seedlings, it is well to treat the seeds themselves with a commercial fungicide obtained from a garden store.

After the seeds have sprouted and grown for a time they will require the addition of a liquid fertilizer which can also be obtained from a garden store. At first the seedlings require no soil nutrients because they live upon food stored within the seeds, but in time this is used up and the tiny plants must obtain mineral elements from the soil.

For merely observing the sprouting of such seeds as beans, peas, and corn, all that is required is that of placing them between layers of moist paper towels in a pan. To watch the progress of germination the upper towels can easily be removed and replaced.

The seeds of conifers (pine, spruce, and fir) can be bought or collected in forests and germinated. The same applies to palm seeds. Such seeds may be planted in pots or seed-flats containing about four inches of woods soil. As a general rule, they should be planted to depths of about two or three times the diameters of the seeds, a rule that applies to nearly all seeds. It is well to first soak the seeds in water for a day or so. This will speed up germination, especially in the case of hard seeds. Do not become impatient; many tree seeds germinate very slowly, often requiring weeks or even months.

The seeds of many wild flowers and trees can be easily germinated and grown in a small, electrically heated greenhouse such as this one.

In dry climates or in rooms where humidity is low it is often desirable to plant seeds in flats or trays having sides high enough so that panes of glass can be laid over the tops. The glass should usually be several inches above the soil. Such an arrangement helps to conserve moisture and, in winter, holds heat. If you are seriously interested in germinating the seeds of wild trees and flowers it may be desirable to purchase a small electric greenhouse such as the one illustrated here. These are not expensive and are most helpful in growing wild plants. They can be obtained from biological supply houses. The fact that they are electrically heated makes them especially desirable when attempting to germinate tropical seeds such as those of palms and cycads or when germinating seeds in winter.

Another way of germinating seeds and growing wild plants is by means of a vivarium or glass box such as an aquarium with a pane of glass over the top. Wild flower seeds collected in fields and forests can be germinated in such a vivarium and later transplanted. Such plants do best when grown in soil from the places where the seeds were collected, but if this is not practical, a mixture consisting of one part light garden soil well mixed with one part sand may be used.

Lotus seeds, above, have very hard coats and may remain alive for a thousand years.

Seed pods of lotus, right, are shaped like sprinkling can nozzles. The seeds are dropped into the water.

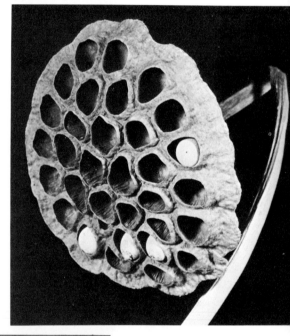

Lotus blooms, below, are among the world's most attractive flowers. They grow in lakes and ponds.

CHAPTER 4

Of Time and Seeds

A thousand years ago there was a lake in Manchuria where sacred, pink lotuses (*Nelumbo nucifera*) bloomed in profusion, adding touches of beauty to the water. When the flowers had been pollinated and had lost their petals, their ovaries grew until they resembled the nozzles of sprinkling cans. When these were mature they contained many marble-like seeds which sank into the mud and were buried. The years passed and the lake dried up, but the lotus seeds remained in the once-wet mud. The centuries passed but the embryos within the seeds remained alive, protected by the flinty seed coats. The world changed, the years of the Crusades came and went, America was discovered, but the lotus seeds slept on in their covering of dry mud.

Eventually the seeds were discovered and placed in a museum where they remained for many more years. Then it occurred to scientists that these ancient seeds might still retain a spark of life. Their seed coats were softened by placing them in strong sulphuric acid, after which they were planted. Amazingly, they sprouted, grew and produced blooms on June 29th, 1952, and continue to bloom each July in the Kenilworth Aquatic Gardens in Washington, D. C. These are blooms out of the past and prove that life may still remain in seeds after great periods of time.

Some of the ancient Manchurian lotus seeds were dated by

Wheat has been cultivated for thousands of years as an important cereal food. At left, close-up of wheat grains. Right, mature wheat beards.

radiocarbon techniques and proved to be more than a thousand years old!

In 1951, three lotus seeds were found in Japan along with the remains of a canoe which was buried twenty feet deep in a lake. Radiocarbon dating was used to determine the age of the canoe and it was found to be 3,075 years, plus or minus 180 years. The seeds, of course, may not have been as old as the canoe. After their hard coats were softened, they germinated. Some scientists believe they will still germinate after many thousands of years.

WHEAT—A CROP WITH A PAST

Wheat has been cultivated by man for thousands of years. It was probably one of the first important food crops planted, and grains of wheat have been found in ancient Egyptian tombs.

There have been many statements regarding the germination

of these wheat grains from the past. In the *Gardeners' Chronicle* for November 11, 1843, it was reported that twelve wheat seeds from a vase in an Egyptian tomb had sprouted and produced twenty-seven new grains of wheat. It was stated that the tomb had been sealed for 3,000 years. Most seed authorities, however, do not believe that wheat will remain alive that long. Wheat grains have undoubtedly been found in ancient tombs, but while these retained their original shapes and were easily recognized as grains of wheat, they dissolved into a black powder when moistened. Grains of both wheat and barley were found in the Saqqara Pyramid where they had been stored for an estimated 5,000 years. No life remained in these seeds, however. Modern radiocarbon dating methods have been used to determine the ages of other wheat and barley grains from Egyptian tombs and they were found to be 6,391 years old, plus or minus 180 years. Most authorities consider that wheat seeds do not normally remain alive for more than about thirty years.

BEAL'S BURIED SEEDS

In autumn of 1879, Professor W. J. Beal of the University of Michigan began an experiment. He collected the seeds of

Seeds of peppergrass (pepperweed). These seeds remained alive for nearly 40 years.

Seeds of mullein. These seeds germinated after 70 years in Beal's tests.

twenty common wild plants and, after mixing them with sand, buried them in bottles. Each bottle contained fifty seeds and the bottles were placed eighteen inches deep and upside down to prevent the entry of water. Dr. Beal then waited for time to have its effect on the seeds. He has since died, but his experiment is still going on.

When germination was tested at the end of the first five years (1884), the seeds of the following plants were all dead: cheatgrass, fireweed, spurge, corn cockle and white clover. By the end of twenty years, common mallow seeds had all died, and dogfennel seeds stayed alive only five more years. By 1909, at the end of the thirtieth year, foxtail grass and chickweed seeds were all dead. When the seeds were tested at the thirty-fifth year, shepherd's purse and mullein were found to have died since the previous test. The fortieth year marked the end of germination for five more of the seed lot: pigweed, ragweed, peppergrass, common plantain and purslane (Portulaca). Two more dropped out of the picture at the fiftieth year: black mustard and smart-

*Mimosa seeds have been
known to germinate after
81 years of storage.*

weed. By the sixtieth year, catchfly seeds had all died, leaving
only evening primrose, yellow dock and moth mullein, which
still germinated in 1950 at the end of seventy years.

While no general conclusions seem possible from this long-
range experiment, it does show that the seeds of many common
plants have a very long life expectancy. It should be noted, however, that Beal's seeds were buried in the earth where they were
in contact with moisture. Seeds remain alive longest when stored
in airtight containers under moderate refrigeration.

DORMANCY OF SEEDS

As we have said, the seeds of most weeds, as well as those of
many cultivated plants, will not germinate at the time they fall
from the plant. This is true even though conditions seem perfect
with respect to temperature and moisture. Some seeds must age
for a time. Many a farmer has been surprised at the sudden appearance of weeds in fields that have been weed-free for many
years. The seeds of these weeds had been present all the time

61

but were waiting for the proper time to germinate. Dr. Beal's famous experiment, of course, proved that many common weed seeds may remain alive for many years. Long-range tests by other scientists, too, have emphasized the long life of many seeds. Dr. A. J. Ewart of Australia made germination tests of over 1,400 kinds of seeds obtained from dried plant specimens in museum herbariums and found that many seeds remained alive for 15 or more years. He found that 49 kinds retained their viability (ability to germinate) for more than 50 years. Thirty-seven of these belonged to the pea family, four were mallows, two were euphorbias, while the rest were scattered among various plant families. Two kinds of seeds, those of *Goodia* and *Hovea* (both legumes), germinated after 105 years.

In France, Dr. Paul Becquerel made tests of some old seeds found in a storage room in the National Museum of Paris. Of two kinds of cassia seeds studied, one was 115 years old and the other 158 years old. Both kinds germinated. He planted ten mimosa seeds which were 81 years old and five of them germinated. Based on the results he obtained, Dr. Becquerel estimated that mimosa seeds would probably live for about 221 years, while cassia seeds might live for 200 years. These latter figures are, of course, merely "educated" guesses. Recent tests of mimosa seeds found in the British Museum showed that they were still alive after 149 years.

Mr. J. H. Turner of the Kew Botanical Garden in England obtained old seeds from several sources and found that one kind of clover seeds germinated after 90 years, sweet clover seeds germinated after 81 years, as did medic seeds that were at least 78 years old.

From the above it is obvious that the seeds of many common plants may remain alive to great age, especially if they are properly stored. The storage of dry seeds in museums is probably more favorable to long life than when planted in damp soil. In general it may be said that seeds buried deep in the soil retain

Seeds of flowering spurge. They may germinate after 50 years.

These are melilotus clover seeds. Some clover seeds live for 100 years.

The down-covered seeds of willows are very short-lived. They must germinate quickly or they will die.

their viability longer than those nearer the surface. Apparently, seeds having hard or thick seed coats can remain dormant longer than those with thin coats. This, of course, is what one would expect.

SHORT LIFE-SPAN SEEDS

Some seeds have very short lives. The seeds of cottonwood trees are released in summer and often fill the air with drifting down. To each bit of down is attached a tiny seed that must fall upon damp soil in order to germinate. These seeds remain alive for only a few days, or at most, a few weeks. They germinate very rapidly and within a few hours after alighting upon moist soil or sand they will produce tiny green leaves. Willows, which belong to the same plant family as the cottonwoods, are also noted for their short life-expectancy. Most kinds of willow seeds lose their viability after a few days but it has been found that their lives can be preserved for nearly a year if they are kept in dry air in a refrigerator.

Seeds of the river maple, at the time they are shed, contain about 58 per cent water and if this high moisture content falls to 30 or 34 per cent they die. It has been found, however, that if they are stored in damp conditions near the freezing point they will remain alive for more than three months. These seeds are shed in spring when weather is apt to be damp. In the case of the sugar maple, on the other hand, which sheds its seeds in autumn when conditions are apt to be dry, the seeds can tolerate complete air-drying. Thus, the lives of the seeds of each kind of maple are adapted to the period of the year when they are shed. Each kind of seed must be adapted in this way if it is to survive. The seeds of wild rice normally fall in the water where they remain until spring when germination occurs. If these seeds are dried, they quickly die. It is also of interest that the water into which wild rice seeds fall must be near the freezing point for a time before germination will occur. This prevents the seeds from germinating at once. Here we see a very clever mechanism in operation which makes sure that the seeds will not only remain

Seeds of wild rice. They remain in icy water until germination occurs.

alive in the water all winter, but will not germinate until spring.

Other seeds besides those mentioned above also have short lives. Grapefruit seeds are injured by drying, as are the seeds of oaks, walnuts, hickories and chestnuts. The seeds of many tropical plants and trees, too, are short-lived. Examples are those of the rubber tree, tea, coconut, palm, royal palm, palmetto and various other palms.

A HANDFUL OF SNUFFBOX BEANS

In August, 1945, I picked up a handful of large beans from the ground in the jungle on the island of Guam. These beans were later identified as snuffbox beans (*Lens phaseoloides*). They are also known by other names; in the Philippines they are called *balones,* in the West Indies *cacoons,* and in Australia, matchbox beans. The plant that produces them has a very wide distribution since the beans have extremely hard seed coats and can stand long immersion in sea water. They are carried about over the world by ocean currents and often washed upon beaches, so they are sometimes called "sea beans."

It is a strange fact that these beans led to the discovery of the Gulf Stream. In the year 1693 some of these sea beans were found washed up on the shore of the Orkney Islands. Their discoverer recorded the incident as follows: "Cast up on the Shoar there are very oft those pretty Nutts, of which they use to make Snuff-boxes." Many years later James Wallace, the naturalist, found the beans growing in Jamaica. He concluded, therefore, that there must be an ocean current flowing across the Atlantic from the West Indies where the beans grew, to the Orkney Islands which lie off the north coast of Scotland. This current was later named the Gulf Stream.

In their native habitats the snuffbox beans grow into large vines with snakelike branches often reaching the size of a man's arm. These vines may climb to the tops of jungle trees a hundred feet tall. When green, they have great strength, and

Snuffbox beans are produced in long pods by a jungle vine. Sometimes they are called "sea beans" because they travel by ocean currents.

are often used for the construction of fish traps. Small pealike flowers are produced and, eventually, there is a large pod about fourteen inches long containing a number of the large seeds. These seeds or beans fall to the forest floor where they await the coming of the rainy season to sprout. Sometimes they are washed into streams and carried down to the sea.

Upon my return to the United States I placed the handful of snuffbox beans in a box in my attic among other souvenirs of my travels. Here they remained for twenty years. During summer, the attic temperatures often reached 120 degrees Fahrenheit. One day the forgotten beans were found and one of them was placed in a flower pot. Two months later a three-foot vine was growing up out of the pot. The snuffbox bean had sprouted after remaining long forgotten in the dry attic. Will it grow into a huge vine as it does in the tropical jungle? Only time can tell.

Winged seeds of maple break apart and spin away when mature.

Zanonia *seeds, with their cellophane-like wings, grow in the jungles of Java. They were the basis for a successful sailplane that was built.*

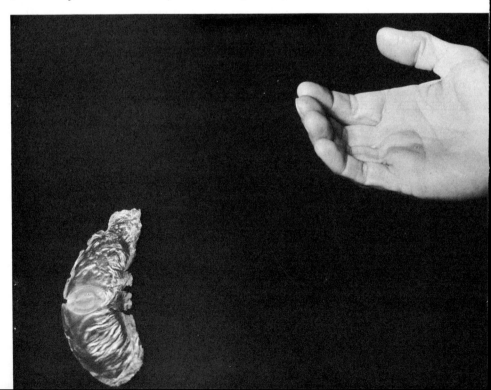

CHAPTER 5

The Travels of Seeds

Without doubt you have noticed the winged seeds of maples spinning down to the ground in autumn whenever a breeze stirred the trees. But did you ever pause to consider why these seeds were equipped with wings? If the seeds fell directly to the ground under the parent tree there would soon be a crowded cluster of maple seedlings, none of which would have room to grow. Thus, Nature has fitted each seed with a wing that makes it spin as it falls, slowing up the fall of the seeds and enabling wind to carry them some distance away.

While still attached to the twigs maple seeds are in pairs but, when they fall, they separate. Seeds bearing wings of this type are called *samaras*. Somewhat similar winged seeds are also found in ash, elm, tree-of-heaven, catalpa and pine. Seeds from tall trees may be carried almost a thousand feet away, but if there are updrafts or rising air currents the seeds may sail much farther. As winged tree seeds fall they spin in characteristic fashions and, if you notice them carefully, you can learn to identify the various seeds by the way in which they spin.

Basswood seeds have an unusual type of wing. These seeds are attached to the undersurface of a leaflike sail that carries them for a considerable distance. In a manner of speaking, they are like little helicopters.

One of the world's most remarkable sailing seeds is that pro-

Left, close-up of a thistle seed parachute showing the feathery filaments that help it float in air. When it strikes an obstacle the seed is dropped. Right, seeds of milkweed with their feather-like parachutes.

duced by a large vine that climbs to the tops of tall trees in Java. This is the *Zanonia* plant and it belongs to the gourd family. When its seeds are mature, they sail away on two cellophane-like wings about five inches across from tip to tip. So efficient are these wings that the seeds glide for long distances. In 1889, a German botanist collected some of these seeds and took them home with him. They excited the interest of sailplane designers who studied their aerodynamic characteristics. It was found that the seeds sailed at 6.7 feet per second and traveled 4.5 feet for each foot of altitude lost. This was considered to be good performance. It was found, also, that when one of the seeds was dropped from a height of 100 feet it sailed away, in still air, to a distance of 450 feet. Sailplane designers were so pleased with the seeds' performance that they built a tail-less sailplane based on the shape of the *Zanonia* seeds. It flew successfully and, naturally, was named "The Zanonia." Thus, man learned how to design a plane from studies of a jungle seed.

Winds blow continually over the face of the earth and anything that floats in them is carried along. Convection currents, or rising columns of heated air, are also responsible for carrying various seeds and small insects to great heights. A great many studies have been made of aerial plankton by means of traps attached to airplanes. Thousands of insects occur at high altitudes as do the fuzzy seeds of plants. Seeds of Joe-Pye weed were trapped at 500 feet, and fleabane and willow seeds at 3,000 feet, although only the willow seeds have special adaptations for such aerial travel. Sow thistle seeds are equipped with tiny parachutes so it is not surprising that they were trapped at 2,000 feet. The most amazing thing, however, was that many grass seeds with no attachments whatever were trapped at great heights. Paspalum seeds, which are smooth and relatively heavy, were trapped at altitudes up to 5,000 feet!

The seeds of many common plants are equipped with special parachutes that enable winds to carry them very easily. The scientific principle involved is the exposure to air currents of large surfaces per units of weight. A seed will float in air if it has attached to it feather-light structures that greatly increase its

Like tiny ballet dancers on a glassy stage, the seeds of wild lettuce (Lactuca) *pirouette upon a pane of glass.*

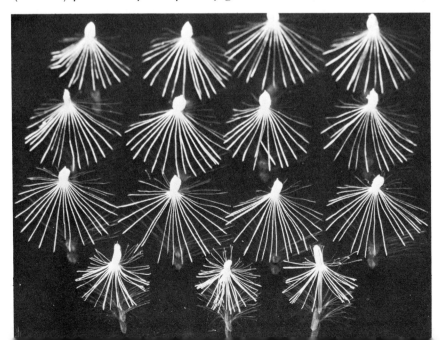

surface. A dandelion seed without its attached bit of down would have little chance of floating in a breeze, but the silky parachute enables it to "fly" with the moving air. When examined under a hand lens, the parachutes of such seeds as dandelions, milkweeds, thistles and goat's-beards are found to be very remarkable structures, indeed. Each filament of the parachute is branched so that an umbrella is formed that "catches" the air very efficiently. It is easily conceivable that such seeds might cross great oceans like the Atlantic. Actually, this has probably occurred, since such plants are worldwide in distribution. Plants are rooted to the earth and cannot travel but they have, in many instances, fitted their seeds to travel great distances.

BY HOOK OR BY CROOK

We have all, at one time or another, returned from a hike and found cockleburs or beggar-ticks stuck to our clothing. We picked these bothersome objects off and tossed them away, probably on the ground. In so doing we were cooperating with the plants from which we picked them up. These spiny seeds hitched a ride and we carried them away and "planted" them in a new location. It was no accident; Nature had planned it that way from the beginning.

Hitchhiking seeds have been securing free rides on the fur and skins of animals and on the feathers of birds for millions of years and it is evidently quite a successful means of travel since so many plants have adopted it. About 10 per cent of the flowering plants secure transportation in this way.

Probably the commonest of these hitchhikers are the seeds of the tick trefoil, a member of the clover family that bears an attractive, small bloom. The pods are constricted between each seed so that, when ripe, the seeds, each in its separate section of the pod, break off and stick to clothing or fur. In Africa there is a plant (*Hedysarum*) with similar habits that has been introduced into the United States and is sometimes encountered in fields. The seed pods of both of the above plants are covered with tiny

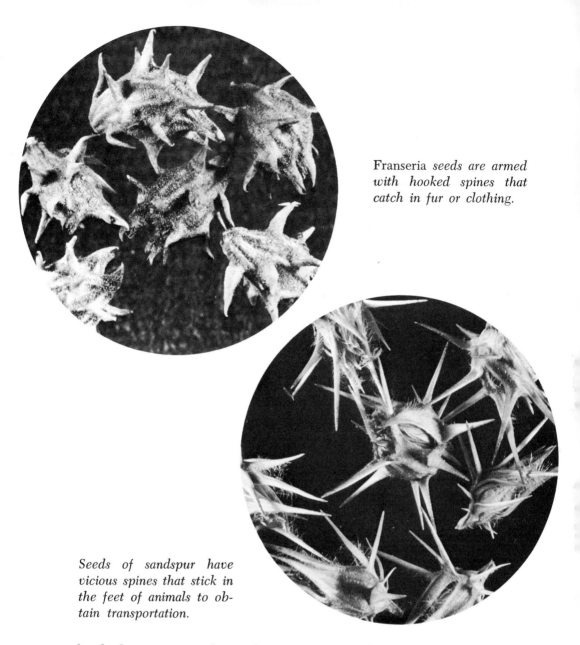

Franseria *seeds are armed with hooked spines that catch in fur or clothing.*

Seeds of sandspur have vicious spines that stick in the feet of animals to obtain transportation.

hooked spines. Similar techniques are employed by stickseed (*Lappula*), bedstraw (*Galium*) and other plants. In the case of beggar-ticks and Spanish needle (*Bidens*), the seeds are fitted with barbed spines at one end.

The seeds of cocklebur (*Xanthium*) are enclosed, two each, in a capsule covered with sharp hooks that, once attached, are very difficult to remove. The seed containers of burdock (*Arctium*) are similarly equipped, though they are easier to remove. The

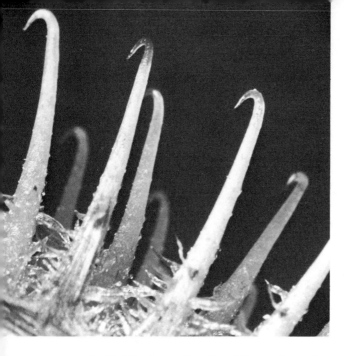

These are greatly enlarged hooked spines on a cockle- bur pod. It is easy to un- derstand how these pods are able to attach them- selves to clothing and fur for transportation.

individual seeds of wild parsley also use hooked spines, as do those of *Franseria* and many other plants.

Among the most "vicious" of all small seed-bearing burs are those of sandspur (*Cenchrus*), a grass found in many areas. These burs are fitted with a number of sharp spines and woe unto him who steps on one with bare feet! Similar sandspurs occur in Europe where they often cause painful wounds in the feet of sheep and other animals.

The unicorn plant (*Martynia*) which grows in several places in southern United States has a most unusual method of attach- ing its seed pods to animals' legs. When dry, the pods are five inches long and have two long, curved arms that have hooks. These can easily grasp the legs of animals.

CREEPERS AND HOPPERS

The seeds of many plants obtain changes in location by methods that would, at first glance, appear to be ineffective. Seeds that creep or hop along the surface of the ground admit- tedly do not travel very far or go very fast, but they move enough to get away from the immediate vicinity of the parent plants. These seeds are caused to creep along the ground by

Sneezeweed seeds are shaped like little darts. Their attached spines and appendages open and close with changes in humidity, causing them to creep slowly along the ground.

means of attached bristles or spines that, alternately, spread apart and close up as humidity varies. This causes the seeds to move very slowly, but they do move. Such techniques are used by a number of plants of the daisy family such as scabiosa, sneezeweed (*Helenium*), blanketflower (*Gaillardia*), bachelor's button (*Centaurea*) and many others. This means of travel is also used by some kinds of clover, such as crimson clover.

The seeds of *Stipa* or needle grass are even more interesting. Each seed has long awns or filaments attached to one end. These awns are very sensitive to changes in humidity and, if the seeds are placed on the ground or on a table, the awns will twist about. As a matter of fact, they will show considerable movement if they are merely breathed upon. In some kinds of these grasses the awns are bent elbow-wise near their tips and the part below the elbow is twisted spirally. Moisture causes the awns to twist and untwist and the seed is pushed about. In one grass, appropriately called "animated oats," there are two awns which twist in opposite directions. As moisture changes cause the awns to twist they press against each other and, when enough tension is built up, they snap, causing the seed to hop a short distance.

Above, Stipa *grass seeds have long tails or awns that twist about, causing them to creep along the ground. Eventually the pointed heads of the seeds are pushed into the soil. Below, crimson clover seed pods look like small insects. Moisture causes their spines to open and close, pushing them along the ground.*

The movements of awns of some grasses also serve another purpose at times. The twisting motion causes the sharp, forward ends of the seeds to push into the ground. Thus, in effect, they plant themselves!

SEED-PLANTING ANTS

Long ago, in the Holy Land, the wise King Solomon observed ants industriously carrying the seeds of plants into their underground nests. He was so impressed that he advised his people to consider the ways of the industrious insects.

The ants observed by Solomon belong to the genus *Messor*

Harvester ant carrying a seed home to its nest

but ants with similar habits occur in the United States. The most interesting of these are the harvester ants (*Pogonomyrmex*) that build large, conical mounds on the Great Plains. In a large harvester ant colony there may often be found a quart or so of stored seeds or "grain." Surrounding the nest cones of these ants there is always a bare, circular area and this is fringed, at its outer edge, by a dense growth of almost all the plants growing in the vicinity. Now it was once believed that the ants planted the seeds of these plants in order that they would have a nearby source of seeds for the future use. While this is an interesting idea, there appears to be no foundation for it. Actually, the

Harvester ants in one of their underground seed bins

plants that grow around harvester ant mounds become established there in two ways: they either grow from seeds accidentally dropped by the foraging ants or from sprouting seeds carried out of the underground tunnels. When heavy rains sweep across the prairies the ants' seed bins become wet and the seeds often sprout. When this occurs, the ants carry the sprouted seeds out to the edge of the cleared space surrounding the mound and discard them. Naturally, many of them grow into plants.

GUNS AND FIRECRACKERS

One day, while collecting seeds from wild plants, I grasped the small seed pod of a flowering spurge between my fingers. I was startled by a snapping sound like that of a small firecracker. Upon further investigation, I discovered that, when the ripe seed pod of one of these plants is touched, it snaps apart, scattering the seeds. Such explosive seed pods are rather common but I had never before encountered this particular one.

In the case of wood sorrel or oxalis, the seeds are enclosed within vertical slits in an elongated seed pod. Each black seed is covered with a slick, gelatinous material and, when the seeds are about ready to be released, the pod begins swelling up with water. When sufficient pressure has built up within the pod, the seeds are snapped out from between the slits like tiny projectiles. This occurs readily, if the pod is touched.

Violets have pods that eject their seeds in a manner similar to that used by the flowering spurge. Upon maturity, violet pods separate into three sections or valves, each of which is more or less boat-shaped. The walls of these valves are made up of several different kinds of cell layers which dry unequally so that the two sides tend to bend and press together. This brings pressure to bear upon the seeds and eventually they snap out at high speed.

A somewhat similar technique is employed by witch hazel.

78

When violet pods are dry the walls of the pods press together causing the seeds to snap out.

Seed pods of flowering spurge push up above the flower as it matures. When dry, the pod snaps open with a sound like a small firecracker, tossing the seeds away from the plant.

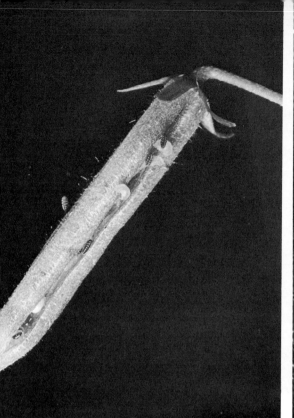

When an oxalis seed pod, left, matures, slits appear in its sides. The seeds, which are enclosed in gelatinous coverings, are snapped out with considerable force. At right, close-up of oxalis seeds.

These shrubs bloom in fall or winter and the seed pods produced in spring have two thick lips between which the black, spindle-shaped seeds rest. As the pods dry out the lips part and great pressure is brought to bear upon the seeds located deeper within the pod. When conditions are right, the seeds shoot out and may travel up to ten feet through the air.

New Jersey tea also uses an explosive pod to shoot out its seeds. The seed pods of this plant consist of three segments with the seeds located in grooves between each segment. As the pods dry, pressure builds up and eventually the seeds are snapped out.

One of the most remarkable of the plants that shoot their seeds are the dwarf mistletoes that live as parasites on pines. The seeds of these plants are quite similar to perfectly streamlined projectiles; that is, they are rounded in front and tapered at the tail end. The seeds are shot out of their pods at an initial acceleration of about 5,000 g's! By contrast, a satellite rocket accelerates at only between five and ten g's. This force causes the seeds to shoot long distances where they may lodge on another tree and grow.

Yet another remarkable method of shooting seeds is that used by the squirting cucumber (*Ecballium*) of Europe. The fruit of this plant resembles a small, spiny cucumber. The stalk fits into the end like a stopper. When ripe, the fruit falls to the ground and, as it continues to ripen, great pressure builds up inside. When this pressure is great enough, the stopper is suddenly forced out, along with the contained seeds, which squirt a considerable distance.

SLINGSHOT SEEDS

Seeds, for their travels, use almost every kind of mechanical device invented by man except wheels. The slingshot technique of tossing seeds is quite common. Probably the best example is that used by the wild geranium. The seeds of these common plants are borne in separate containers located around a central

Wild geranium seeds are contained in tiny cups which have springs. When the cups snap loose the seeds are tossed some distance away.

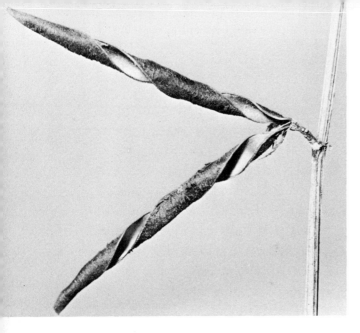

The two halves of vetch seed pods snap apart with a twisting motion which causes the seeds to be propelled away.

stalk or column. Each seed container is attached to the central column by a flexible spring. While undergoing maturity the five seed containers are anchored to the base of the column but, as they dry, tension gradually builds up in the "springs" and, eventually, the seed containers break loose and snap outward, projecting the seed away through the air.

Sometimes it is a little difficult to classify properly the seed-projecting mechanism used by a plant. In the case of vetch, the two halves of the pods, when dry, snap open and toss the seeds away. Whether one should call this an explosive or a slingshot method is an open question.

Bitter cress (*Cardamine*) is a common little weed in many localities. It belongs to the mustard family. When its seed pods are mature they are about an inch long and of slender form. Each pod consists of a central, transparent wall and of two side walls or sections that fit against it, one on either side. The seeds are enclosed between these. At the proper time during their development, the enclosing walls of the pods suddenly roll upward causing the seeds to snap away with considerable force. In fact, if your hand is brushed against a bitter cress plant when its pods are mature, the seeds can be felt striking it. The jewel-weed (*Impatiens*) uses a similar seed-tossing trick. The principle

The seeds of Cardamine *grow in elongate pods. When disturbed, the sides of the pods coil upward, flipping the seeds away.*

is the same as that of a watch spring. There are five strap-shaped springs that fit together forming the seed pod. As the pod grows and the seeds become mature tension builds up in the five segments of the pod and, eventually, these will fly apart at the slightest touch and scatter their contained seeds. This plant is sometimes called touch-me-not, and in the event that the explosive seed pod is not touched, it will "explode" by itself. When this occurs the entire pod sails through the air, firing its seeds in all directions as it goes.

There are many other plants that use slingshot methods of dispersing their seeds. The seed pods of these plants are usually located in such a position on the plants that leaves will not interfere with the flight of the seeds. Indeed, in some plants the pods are pushed outward from the plant to an exposed position shortly before the seeds are ready to be ejected.

Anyone who has ever walked along a sea beach has noticed the miscellaneous collection of debris tossed up by the waves. This consists of an astonishing variety of objects from strands of seaweed and marine shells to driftwood, as well as grapefruit skins thrown overboard from ocean liners. If one searches carefully among this array of ocean discards he is apt to find large seeds or "sea beans," especially along tropical beaches. These sea beans may have been carried by currents for hundreds or even thousands of miles.

The oceans of the world are restless and, in addition to their regular tidal movements, they flow in definite paths across the earth. Any object—even a seed—that falls into the ocean may be transported a long way and eventually washed up on some foreign shore. If one studies the distribution of the world's vegetation it becomes obvious that ocean currents have had much to do with plant geography. It is believed, for example, that the original home of the coconut palm was the western coast of Central America, but ocean currents, long ago, carried floating coconuts to almost every continent and island where they could possibly germinate and grow.

I once had the good fortune to spend some time in the South Pacific. There I became familiar with many tropical plants that I never expected to see again. Later, I was surprised to see these same plants growing wild in the tropical portion of Florida. We say that the earth is growing smaller because of our increased use of air travel, but, to the world's plants, the earth has always been small. While some seeds are injured by submersion in salt water, many others seem unharmed. The seeds of one kind of gourd (*Legenaria*) are unharmed by submersion in salt water for as long as a year.

Coconuts and sea beans have special adaptations that fit them for water travel. Coconuts have air-filled husks or "life preservers" while many sea beans have air spaces within their hard seed

This Macuna *bean from Central America (photographed in two positions) was washed ashore along the Gulf Coast.*

The nut of the coconut is surrounded by a layer of air-filled fiber that enables it to float across seas and oceans.

Sea beans washed ashore from the ocean sometimes sprout and grow.

coats to give them buoyancy. In Nature's economy it is an advantage to a plant to have a wide distribution. If they die out in one place they are apt to survive somewhere else.

THE TUMBLERS

There are yet other plants that leave the places where they grew and carry their seeds "in person" to the new locations. These are the "tumbleweeds," of which there are many kinds. Such plants, when full grown, break loose from the soil and roll over the ground, scattering their seeds as they go.

Probably the first of these plants to be observed was the "Rose of Jericho" (*Anastatica hierochuntica*). The botanical name means "resurrection plant from Jericho," but it is more or less rose-shaped. These strange plants were first observed by the Crusaders during the Middle Ages and many stories were told about them. The Rose of Jericho is a small plant, about six inches high, that grows on the sandy deserts of Arabia, Syria and Algeria. It belongs to the mustard family. After flowering, the leaves fall off and the plant dries up and rolls itself up into a ball. Within the protective framework formed by the outer, dried stems, are found the seed pods. These dry, ball-like plants are uprooted by winds and blown across the landscape. When rains occur, the balls unfold and spread out exposing the seed

A snuffbox bean sawed in half reveals the air space that keeps it afloat.

Tumbleweeds, when mature, break away from the soil and roll long distances, scattering their seeds.

pods and the seeds are released. It is believed by some that "the rolling thing before the whirlwind" mentioned in Isaiah was, in truth, the Rose of Jericho.

Plants that scatter their seeds by tumbleweed tactics usually live in open dry areas where they can easily be rolled about by winds. On our western plains, during high winds, I have seen tumbleweeds bounding across the landscape like hundreds of sheep on the run. Sometimes these dry, spherical plants, which are often two feet in diameter, accumulate in deep gullies to depths of fifty feet. Our American tumbleweed or Russian thistle (*Salsola*) is widely distributed on the plains and in the Rocky Mountains. There is another, smaller, western tumbleweed, known as the delicate tumbleweed (*Cycloloma*). Tumbleweeds of other kinds occur in various other plains areas of the world. On the Russian steppes there are the wind-witches—tumble-

Mistletoe seeds are sticky and adhere to the feet and beaks of birds. When the birds fly to other trees the seeds are rubbed off and grow as parasites.

weeds that often become locked together in large balls many feet in diameter and bound across the open plains.

While most tumbleweeds roll about in order to scatter their seeds, there are a few tumbling plants that actually take root again and grow if they arrive at suitable spots.

ANIMAL TRANSPORTATION

What better way could Nature have developed to transport seeds than that of using animals to carry them? This is done by coating seeds with glue to make them adhere to their bodies or by enticing birds to eat them or carry them away in their beaks. For example, the seeds of common mistletoe are produced in white berries. Birds feed upon these berries and the adhesive seeds often stick to their beaks. The birds then fly away, perhaps to other trees, and rub the seeds off upon the bark where they germinate, sending their parasitic sinkers or "roots" down into the living wood to absorb nourishment.

Migrating birds fly from continent to continent and, if seeds adhere to their feet or feathers or are present within their digestive tracts, they may be carried along. Many aquatic plants have very small seeds which may easily stick to the mud on birds' feet. Charles Darwin once collected 6¾ ounces of mud

The pretty scarlet seeds of magnolia are pushed out of the cone and hang suspended by fine threads. Thus they are easily seen by birds.

from the feet of water birds and placed it in a container and watered it. From this mud, 537 plants grew, thus proving how efficiently the seeds of aquatic plants can be carried from place to place by birds in their travels. I know of a large, artificial lake that was built far from any other body of water. Within a few years, almost every type of aquatic plant had become established. There are actually some seeds that will not germinate unless they have first passed through animals' digestive systems. Many weed seeds become established in fields in this way. Tomato and persimmon seeds are uninjured by passing through animal digestive systems, while the germination of barberry seeds is improved.

Other seeds with sticky seed coats are those of flax and some cacti. When these seeds become moist their gelatinous coverings become sticky and they can easily be carried by animals. We saw how the squirting cucumber ejects its seeds. These seeds are sticky and if some animal disturbs the cucumber when it is ready to squirt its seeds, they stick to its body or legs and are carried away.

One of the cleverest methods used by any plant to obtain transportation of its seeds is that used by the magnolia tree. The seeds of this tree are contained in cones and as these mature the pretty, scarlet seeds are pushed out and hang invitingly suspended on slender threads so that birds can easily see them.

SALT SHAKERS AND SKI JUMPERS

Some plants get along very well with less spectacular methods of seed dispersal. A large number of common flowering plants have erect seed pods that scatter seeds about when the plant is buffeted by wind or disturbed by the passage of a large animal. An easily observed example is the seed pod of poppy. The seed pods of this plant are globular with attractive "lids." As the pod matures and becomes dry, the "lid" pushes upward exposing many small slits. If such a dry pod on its long stalk is violently disturbed its contained seeds are scattered about. The effect is much like salt being shaken out of a salt shaker. Columbine uses a similar dispersal technique as do iris, primrose and many other plants.

Many plants use what may best be described as "ski-jumping" methods of tossing their seeds. There is no complicated snapping or catapulting mechanism involved, yet the seeds may be tossed some distance away. Probably the easiest of the ski-jump plants to observe is salvia or sage. After pollination occurs and the corolla tube withers and drops off, there remains the calyx tube within which the seeds are anchored. The lower lip of the calyx curves upward at its tip like a ski jump. When the seeds are mature and ready to be shed they remain lightly attached to the back of the calyx tube. Any disturbance such as that caused by a passing animal or a wind causes the plant to shake and the calyx tube to nod violently. When this occurs, the seeds break loose and roll down the calyx tube. The motion of the plant causes the seeds, as they roll down, to be tossed some distance. Since the calyx tubes are all pointed away from the stalk the seeds follow a trajectory aimed away from the plant.

A close relative of sage, germander (*Teucrium*), employs a similar seed-tossing technique. There are stiff hairs or bristles

90

Sweetgum seeds are contained in "balls" suspended from the twigs. Winds swing the "balls" and scatter the small seeds.

As poppy seed pods mature the central portion pushes upward exposing numerous openings. Winds scatter the seeds about.

within the calyx tube of germander which apparently give the seeds spinning motions. Thus, they have the same effect as the grooves in a rifle barrel which cause the bullets to spin and follow a straight course through the air.

JOHNNY APPLESEED

Ancient travelers to far lands often brought seeds back to their native countries and planted them. In this way, important food plants and attractive flowers became established, perhaps thousands of miles from their native habitats.

Probably the best known of recent travelers who came to appreciate the value of seeds and the things they can do for mankind was John Chapman, better known as Johnny Appleseed. He is, in many ways, an early American legend and it is difficult to separate the facts from the folktales that have grown up around his life.

Born on the Nashua River near the city of Leominster, Massachusetts, in the year 1774, he grew up on the frontier and, for a time, homesteaded in Pennsylvania. But he was a wanderer at heart and unwilling to lead a settled life. He was also a teller of tall tales regarding his lonely travels and experiences on the wild frontier. Just when the planting of apple seeds entered his life as a major obsession is unknown but in 1804, when he was

The curved lower lip of the calyx tube of salvia serves as a ski jump. The seeds break loose, roll down the calyx tube and away through the air.

Greatly enlarged apple seeds. Apples were grown in Europe thousands of years ago and their seeds were brought to America by early settlers.

thirty years old, he began clearing small patches of land near Franklin, Pennsylvania, and planting them with apple seeds obtained from cider mills. As to who actually owned the land where he planted his seeds he cared little; it seemed sufficient that they grew and bore fruit. In the mind of Johnny Appleseed there developed a fixed idea that what the settlers especially needed was apples. Foods, especially those that might be classed as luxuries, were scarce. The seedling apples planted by Johnny Appleseed were of low quality by present standards but they did fulfill an important frontier need. Slowly he wandered back and forth across the thinly settled land, always with a buckskin bag of apple seeds on his back, planting them here and there in suitable locations and later tending his orchards. As far as is known he never accepted pay for his services. "The bees work without wages; why should I not do the same?"

Thus, for the last forty-six of his seventy-two years of life, Johnny Appleseed wandered through the American wilderness planting apple seeds as he went. He died in 1847, and at the site of his birthplace stands a granite monument with an inscription that reads: "He planted seeds that others might enjoy the fruit."

Mexican jumping beans are produced by a Mexican spurge with poisonous sap. When heated, caterpillars within the "beans," which are actually seed pods, cause them to hop about.

If a Mexican jumping bean is cut open one can see the small caterpillar inside that causes the bean to skip around when it moves.

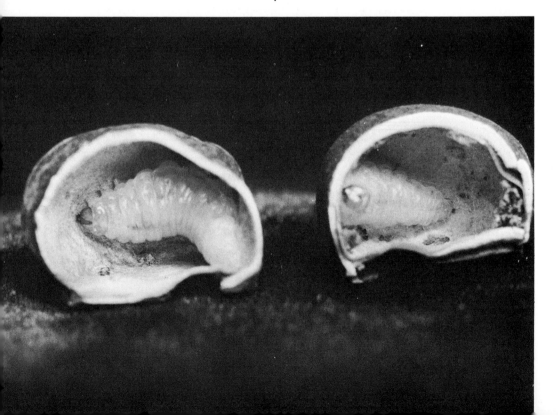

CHAPTER 6

Some Uncommon Seeds

*M*any years ago, travelers returning from Mexico often brought strange, hopping "beans" home with them. When heated or placed on a warm surface these seeds obligingly jumped about in a mysterious manner. Very few people ever went to the trouble to determine what it was that caused the movements. Eventually, of course, it was found that within the seed coat of each bean there was a small caterpillar or moth larva and that this insect was somehow responsible for the jump in the jumping bean. But the story back of these unusual objects is even more interesting than the jumping beans themselves.

The plant that produces the jumping beans grows in the dry barrancas and arroyos in the region of the Rio Mayo in the Mexican states of Sonora and Chihuahua. It is a small shrub with shiny lance-shaped leaves and attractive flower spikes that appear in early summer when rains come to the arid land. It is at this time that a small moth, closely related to the codling moth that infests apples, appears and deposits her eggs in the young seed pods. This is the jumping bean moth (*Laspeyresia saltitans*), and her larvae or caterpillars can live in no other plant. The plant or shrub itself is a spurge (*Sebastiania pringlei*), known locally as *yerba de flecha* meaning "arrow plant." It is called this because its milky, poisonous sap was once used by Indians as an arrow poison.

When the three-parted pods of the arrow plant are mature they snap open, tossing the seeds through the dry vegetation with a sound like BB shot. Many of the pods, however, do not contain seeds for the simple reason that the moth larvae have consumed them. These pods fall to the ground. The desert sun heats the sand causing the caterpillars within the "beans" to jerk their bodies. By the time the caterpillars are mature they have lined the inner surfaces of their "beans" with silk and when stimulated by the desert heat they anchor their feet in the silk and flip their bodies. Since the pods are light in weight, the motions of the insects cause them to skip about. As long as the "bean" or seed pod is exposed to the hot sun the insect continues to jerk. Eventually, the pod, in a hit-or-miss fashion, reaches a spot of shade and the caterpillar settles down to rest. It would thus seem that the "beans" jump about to avoid the hot sun, though eventually, of course, the caterpillars all pupate or go into their resting stages and no longer cause the "beans" to hop. Mexican jumping beans purchased in novelty stores go through the same transformation, which accounts for the fact that they eventually all cease their movements. If the "beans" are kept in a closed container it will be noticed that small moths emerge through little round holes in the "beans."

FISH-POISON NUTS

In some tropical countries, roots of *derris* plants are used to catch fish. When pounded up and placed in streams, a substance in them called *rotenone* stupefies and kills fish but leaves them fit for human food. We use this same substance or chemical as an insecticide.

On the various islands of the South Pacific the natives make use of yet another plant poison to kill fish. The tide pools in the coral reefs surrounding most of the atoll islands abound with fishes in great abundance and diversity. Many are beautifully colored in every hue of the rainbow and look like butterflies as

Barringtonia nuts contain a narcotic substance that stupefies fish, enabling natives to capture them.

they dart through the clear water among the corals. These reef fish are difficult to catch with a net or a spear, but the natives long ago discovered that the meat of *Barringtonia* nuts, if mashed up and placed in the tide pools, would soon kill them yet leave them edible.

Barringtonia nuts grow on very stately trees that resemble our native magnolia, even to the shape and texture of their leaves. The flowers have four white petals and dense tufts of crimson-tipped stamens. When mature, the fruit consists of a pyramid-shaped husk within which is contained the nut. The fruit is about three inches in diameter. Like sea beans, Barringtonia fruits are very buoyant and, since the trees often grow near the sea, the nuts fall in the water and float away. In this way the trees became established on other islands and the tree is thus widely distributed in the Pacific area where it is known by various local names. On Guam it is known to the natives as *puting*, in the Philippines as *botong*, and on Tahiti as *fudu*.

THE BETEL NUT

Like the habit of chewing tobacco in our own country, the

97

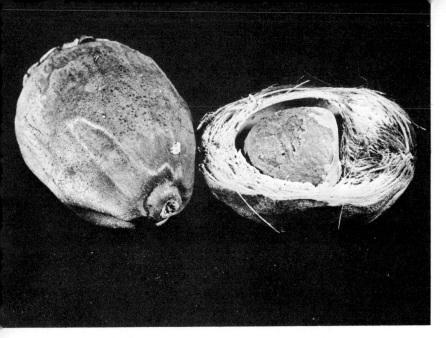

Betel nuts are the fruit of the Areca *palm.*

natives of many tropical lands have the habit of chewing betel nuts (pronounced "beetle"). These nuts are produced by the *Areca* palm (*Areca cathecu*), a handsome member of the palm family that grows in many places in the Tropics.

The nuts, or seeds, of the *Areca* palm resemble miniature coconuts, being about the size of hen eggs. They are borne in clusters suspended below the dark-green fronds and, like the coconut, the nut is enclosed within a fibrous husk. The meat of the nut has a pungent, aromatic odor resembling that of nutmeg and contains a narcotic called *arecaine*. Actually, these nuts are poisonous, but it is like nicotine from the tobacco plant. Tobacco is chewed or smoked, yet nicotine in concentrated form is highly poisonous. In India, betel nut has been used for a long while as a medicine. For this reason betel nuts have long been an item of commerce in the Malay Archipelago.

In chewing betel nut, the saliva is stained red and the teeth eventually turn black and are injured in other ways. It gives a feeling of mild stimulation and well-being and, outside of the harm to teeth, seems to have no ill effects. In former years, betel nut chewing was often a ceremonial ritual at weddings and

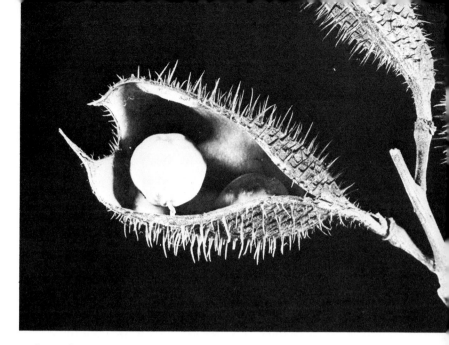

Molucca beans, or sea beans, in their spiny pod

other special occasions. Visitors were always offered betel nut, much as the American Indians passed around the peace pipe as a symbol of hospitality and friendship.

MOLUCCA BEANS

Molucca beans (*Guilandina crista*) are also called sea beans sometimes since they, like many other large, tropical seeds, are often carried by ocean currents, washed up on distant beaches, and are widely distributed in the Tropics. This particular bean is called *pakao* on Guam, *anaoso* on Samoa, *Kakalaioa* in Hawaii, and *calambit* in the Philippines. It also occurs in southern Florida where it is called Molucca bean or nickernut. Sometimes they are also called bezoar nuts.

These large seeds or beans are produced by a shrubby tree with widely spreading branches that are armed with recurved spines. In fact, the Hawaiian name, *Kakalaioa*, means "thorny." The plant bears an attractive, yellow bloom. The seeds, when mature, are enclosed in a spiny pod, there usually being two seeds to each pod. As in the case of the other so-called sea beans, there is an air space in each one to enable it to float.

In former years the bitter meat of these nuts or beans was used as a remedy for malarial fever. For this reason they were once called "fever nuts." On some islands the natives use them as beads.

ABRUS BEANS

In southern Florida there grows a climbing vine with its leaves divided into many small leaflets like those of mimosa. It produces clusters of small purple or white blooms, and may be encountered in almost any wooded area of the tropical parts of Florida. During the day the leaflets are spread flat to absorb the rays of the sun but, like the leaflets of mimosa, they fold up at night. The leaflets are so sensitive to light that they "go to sleep" or fold up even on very cloudy days, opening again when the sun comes out. For this reason it is often called the "weather plant."

The *Abrus* vine is unimportant as vines go, but it has one especially interesting feature. After the blooms have faded, clusters of pods are produced which contain beautiful scarlet and black beans with very glossy surfaces. These are probably the most attractive of all plant seeds, but, in this case, appearance is deceiving. These beautifully colored beans contain a violently poisonous alkaloid that, if injected under the skin, will cause death. When eaten, the seeds also have toxic qualities. In pharmacy, the seeds are known as jequirity beans. The poisonous material they contain is very similar to that found in the venom of some poisonous snakes. In India the seeds were once ground into powder and smeared on daggers which could then cause instant death. In our laboratory in the Tropics one of the workers was once perforating the pretty beans with a hot needle to make a string of beads. The needle accidentally pricked his finger with the result that his entire hand became seriously swollen. Strangely, the poison is destroyed by heating so the beans were, at one time, used as human food in Egypt, espe-

The scarlet and black Abrus *beans are probably the most attractive of all seeds, but they are very poisonous.*

cially when other foods were scarce. The roots of the *Abrus* bean plant have a licorice-like taste and have been used as a poor substitute for that flavoring material. The plant is known in India and Australia as wild licorice.

In various places in the Tropics these beans are known under

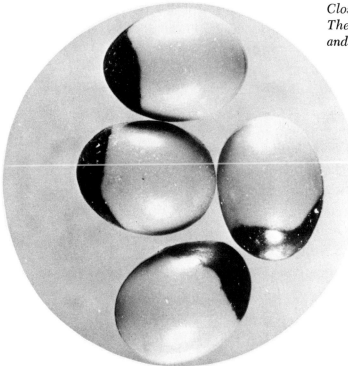

Close-up of Abrus *beans. They are uniform in size and weight.*

various names; in some places they are called coral beads, in other places they are called crab's-eye beans. To the Chamorros of the Philippines they are "*corales*." In India they have been known for centuries and were once used by jewelers and druggists as weights since each bean weighs almost exactly one grain. In former years, they were also strung on strings and used as rosaries; thus they are also called "rosary beans."

THE COCONUT

If you were to ask a number of friends which they considered to be the world's most useful tree you would probably receive a variety of answers. Some would say the oak with its useful wood. Others would give preference to the pines and conifers since the various kinds are so widespread and furnish us with most of our lumber. But the answers would probably ignore the stately coconut palm, since few of us have spent our lives in the lands where these trees are native. To a large proportion of the world's population the coconut is truly the staff of life. The islander dwelling in the empty reaches of the ocean could not live without coconut trees. They furnish him with food and drink as well as with wood for construction of dwellings. In time of hurricanes he seeks safety in the tall trees, often lashing himself and his family to them until the angry winds and waters subside.

Commercially, the coconut is most important. Each nut contains, within its shell, a layer of white meat and a pint or so of sweet, refreshing "milk." The nut, in turn, is enclosed within a fibrous husk so that the entire fruit weighs ten or fifteen pounds. When mature, the nuts are harvested and the husks removed by striking them upon sharpened stakes driven into the ground. The meat is then removed and placed in the sun to dry. This is the *copra* of commerce and the traveler returning from the Tropics will long remember the smell of copra drying on docks in the sun. It is one of the sights and smells of the Tropics.

Fresh coconut meat contains about 40 per cent oil and about

The fibrous layer within a coconut contains air spaces and enables it to float. The meat has been removed from this coconut.

10 per cent carbohydrate, the rest being water. The oil is extracted and made into the finest soaps and cooking oils: (In former years coconut oil was used for illumination in many tropical areas.) In places where coconut trees grow, coconut meat is ground up and fed to domestic animals, including cats and dogs. It is also used in cooking, and taro and other foods are cooked in the milk. From the sap, obtained by cutting the stalks to which the nuts are attached, is made a fermented drink or toddy called "tuba."

The shells and fibers are used as well. On some of the more primitive islands the shells are used as water and oil vessels. In this case, the meat is removed through one of the "eyes," leaving a convenient container. Cups and spoons are also made of the shells. Coconut fiber is used for stuffing cushions, as a fiber for lashing together the framework of native houses, and for weaving mats. In some places in the Tropics, even the roots are used. These contain a drug similar to that found in betel nuts and are chewed for the same purpose.

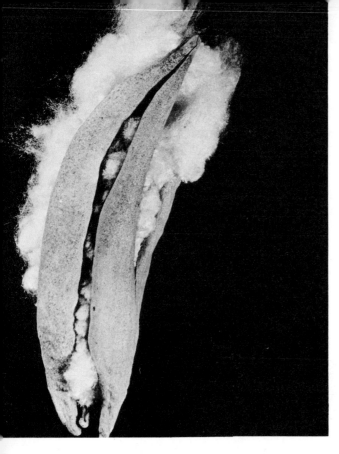

The fruit of the kapok tree is a cotton-filled pod. Kapok cotton or fiber is used in life preservers, but cannot be spun into thread.

Many plants have useful seeds or nuts, but few trees furnish so many different things useful to mankind as does the coconut.

THE SILK-COTTON TREE

When we think of cotton most of us picture fields of cotton with their bolls opening white in the summer sun. But there is yet another kind of cotton produced by trees in Tropical lands. These are the ceiba trees that produce pods filled with fiber-covered seeds. This "cotton" is the kapok of commerce, which is a brownish, fluffy material with a silky texture, and the trees that produce it are sometimes called silk-cotton trees. Unfortunately, this kapok or silk-cotton cannot be used for spinning. Its chief use is as stuffing for pillows and life preservers, for which it is ideal since it has the quality of being very resilient and does not mat as does ordinary cotton. Kapok fiber is very inflammable and, in India, is sometimes used in making fireworks. During

World War II, when the supply of kapok was limited, other sources of stuffing for life preservers had to be explored, and it was found that milkweed fiber was an admirable substitute.

Silk-cotton trees grow in many places in the Tropics. The name "ceiba" is the old native name for the tree in Central America and the West Indies and was adopted as the botanical name. There are several different species, but the most important silk-cotton tree, and the one that grows to greatest size, is the one sometimes grown as an ornamental tree in southern California and Florida. These trees often reach heights of a hundred feet, but their most striking feature is their spreading, buttress-like roots extending above ground. They slope away from the tree like graceful, curving walls and are often several feet high near the tree but fall away, perhaps for thirty feet, to ground level. There is a remarkable specimen of this tree on the island of New Providence, Nassau, with buttress roots ten feet high. The wood of the silk-cotton tree, however, is soft and white and very brittle so it has but little commercial use.

Close-up of kapok seeds with the fibers removed

Banyan seeds are very tiny, being about the size of radish seeds.

THE BANYAN AND ITS SEEDS

There are many different kinds of banyans and they are all closely related to the common fig and the rubber tree. Like the fig, their fruit consists of fleshy receptacles within which are contained numerous small seeds. But the fruits of the banyans have no food value.

It is the method of germination of banyan seeds that is of special interest. The small seeds normally become lodged on the sides of other trees; in southern Florida this is often on the rough trunks of sabal palms. These seeds germinate, sending fine rootlets into the bark or fiber covering the trunk. These rootlets anchor the young plant which then produces a small stem and some leaves. For some time the banyan seedling is satisfied to grow on the side of a tree. It is not a parasite and does not obtain nourishment from the living tree, but merely uses the "host" tree as a place to grow. You might well ask what advantage this is to the young banyan. Any seedling that grows upon the ground is in direct competition with other plants for root space and for sun. The seedling banyan, high above the ground, is removed from competition with other plants at a time when it is at a

Left, a banyan plant. If banyan seeds lodge on the side of another tree they germinate and grow, sending long roots down to the ground. In time the "host" tree (right) is strangled by the entwining banyan roots.

tender age. But the young banyan is not satisfied for long to remain growing upon the side of another tree. Soon it produces long roots which rapidly extend downward to the ground where they enter the soil. The banyan is then, for a time, like a climbing vine that creeps up a tree. Gradually, more and more roots grow down to the ground and the trunk of the banyan slowly enlarges and encircles the host tree. Year by year it increases in size and gradually smothers the tree that once gave it support. In time the host tree dies, leaving the banyan to go on living. For this reason banyans are often called strangler figs.

As time passes banyan trees continue to grow until many of them reach enormous size. There is a banyan tree in the botanical garden in Calcutta that is believed to be more than a hundred years old. Its main trunk, when measured a number of years ago, was 42 feet around and there was 232 additional, prop-trunks, some of which measured more than three feet in diameter. The total circumference of the area covered by this great tree was 850 feet! It is said that the banyan under which Alexander the Great once camped sheltered 7,000 men. This tree, apparently still living, now measures 2,000 feet in circumference and is supported by 3,000 individual trunks or prop-roots.

A LIVING FOSSIL

There are a number of plants still living today that, by all the rules of evolution, should have been extinct for millions of years. Why these particular plants have survived while others passed away is something of a mystery. Perhaps they were simply better adapted and so continued on down the eons.

One group of these so-called "living fossils" are the cycads that came into being during the Carboniferous Age about 300 million years ago. For millions of years they were the dominant form of plant life. As a matter of fact, they gave their name to the Carboniferous Age, which is sometimes known as the Age of Cycads. Some of the early cycads were vinelike. For a long while it was believed that certain fossil fronds found in ancient stone were those of ferns; then about 1900 it was decided that fossil seeds found with them had actually been produced by them. Ferns do not produce seeds; thus scientists decided that the fossil "ferns" were actually ancient seed ferns or cycads.

For many millions of years the cycads flourished in the ancient world, then gradually decreased in importance. Today they occur only in the Tropics or are grown in greenhouses as ornamental plants. Their palmlike foliage is dark green and glossy.

These are the large seeds of the cycad, a fernlike tree that originated many millions of years ago. Cycads now grow only in tropical countries.

There are about a hundred different species or kinds of cycads and they resemble palms; as a matter of fact, most people consider them to be a kind of palm. Usually they are of small size, seldom reaching heights of more than twenty feet. In many tropical lands they are known as tree ferns. In southern Florida there are cycads belonging to the genus *Zamia*, which have thick, tuberous, underground stems containing large amounts of starch. The sexes are borne on separate plants and the large cones contain numerous large, angular seeds which are poisonous when ripe. This poison, however, is dissolved out by soaking in water and the seeds may then be eaten. In some tropical countries the seeds are considered very delicious since their taste resembles that of chestnuts. As proof of the poisonous nature of the nuts, chickens that drink the water in which the seeds have been soaked are often killed. Natives usually prepare the nuts by grinding them on a stone slab or *metate* and the resulting meal is then mixed with water and baked. While this food (*fadang*) can be eaten, it is said to be harmful if eaten continuously, and thus it is used only when other foods are scarce.

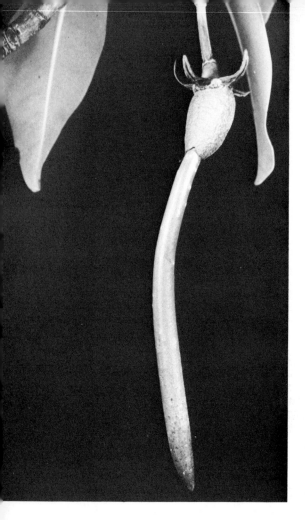

Mangrove seeds germinate while still attached to the tree, producing long, sharp-pointed root-spears. These drop off and grow into new mangroves.

SPEAR SEEDS OF THE MANGROVE

One of the world's most remarkable seeds is that produced by the mangrove, a spreading shrub that forms impenetrable tangles along many tropical coasts, including those of southern Florida. There are a number of different kinds but the one that thrives in Florida is the red mangrove, *Rhizophora mangle*. This shrub, sometimes called a tree, grows with its roots in salt or brackish water which is quite unusual since most trees or land plants are injured by salt. Along the margins of islands and land masses the mangrove spreads, stretching out its roots like the legs of great spiders. These branch and rebranch, each root extending down into the shallow water to attach itself. Silt and sand collect among the roots and gradually new land is formed.

Thus, the mangroves push outward toward the sea, creating new land as they go. For this reason, they have been called "mothers of islands."

At certain seasons the mangrove produces pale yellow, nodding flowers and these, in turn, give rise to small, leathery fruit. This fruit contains a seed that germinates while still on the tree. Gradually, a "root" or *radicle* grows out of the bottom of the fruit and continues to increase in size until it is about ten inches in length. This "root" or root-spear is green and dart-shaped with a pointed tip. In Florida and other places, mangroves can be seen with dozens of these root-spears suspended from their branches. In time the root-spears fall from the tree and penetrate the mud like sharpened stakes. Eventually these take root and grow, forming new mangrove trees. Now it may happen that the water beneath the parent mangrove is too deep for the root-spear to stick in the bottom. When this occurs it bobs back to the surface and floats away in a horizontal position and may be carried by currents to distant islands. As the root-spear drifts along, its center of gravity slowly shifts until it hangs point downward. When it, by chance, drifts into shallow water it sticks in the mud or sand and starts growing. Thus, in effect, it plants itself, perhaps on a distant shore.

Here you can see three mangrove root-spears that have fallen and pierced the mud beneath the parent tree. They will take root and grow.

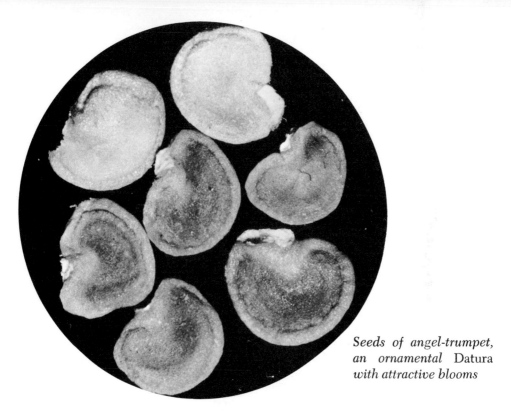

Seeds of angel-trumpet, an ornamental Datura with attractive blooms

Datura, *or jimson weed, belongs to the nightshade family which also contains tomato, pepper, potato, and other edible plants. All parts of the jimson weed, including the seeds, contain poisons.*

CHAPTER 7

Some Evil Seeds

*W*hile most seeds contain abundant stores of starches, proteins and other foods and are thus highly nutritious, there are some kinds that are poisonous. Indeed, some of these seeds are so poisonous that the eating of only one may kill a person.

JIMSON WEED

Jimson weed (*Datura stramonium*) is a common weed of abandoned fields and lots. It is easily recognized by its wide-spreading branches, large, oval leaves with toothed margins, and by its large, spiny fruit. When crushed, the leaves and green fruit have a very pungent and disagreeable odor and for this reason it is also called stinkweed. This plant was one of the first that the Pilgrims had contact with after their disastrous first winter in America. With the arrival of spring they ate the leaves of *Datura* to supplement their food supply, with disastrous results since the plants are very poisonous. Several Pilgrims and some Indians were killed. The name "jimson weed" was actually derived from its original name, Jamestown weed. All parts of the plant, including the seeds, are highly poisonous since they contain an alkaloid called *hyoscyamine*. Children have been killed by eating the green fruit, and some people are so sensitive to the plant that skin irritation is caused by mere contact with the leaves. An important drug called *atropine* is extracted from

113

Seeds of dock (Rumex)

jimson weed. Due to its poisonous nature it is also known as the mad-apple plant and, because of its tubular blooms it is also called Devil's Trumpet.

DOCK

The buckwheat family contains a strange collection of plants, including edible buckwheat, smartweeds, rhubarb and dock. There are many different kinds of dock (*Rumex*) but they are all easily recognized by their spikes of small, greenish flowers that do not really look like flowers at all. Farmers and home owners are usually unhappy about dock since it is a pest weed in fields and on lawns.

While the docks are not usually considered to be poisonous plants, they do contain, especially in their leaves, a poisonous substance (*rumicin*) that sometimes makes animals sick. For a long while Rumex has been listed among drugs as a tonic and astringent. It has also been used to destroy parasites or lice on the skin.

114

The castor-bean plant (*Ricinus*) is often grown in this country for its attractive foliage. The large, star-shaped leaves are often reddish in color and are borne on a tall stalk that, in this country, may reach a height of ten feet, but in Tropical countries grows into a small tree up to thirty feet tall. Its flowers are inconspicuous but the large seeds are enclosed in spiny burs. These seeds are most interesting since they are marked with contrasting blotches and streaks. While these seeds are pleasing in appearance they are very poisonous and many people have been killed or made ill from eating even small pieces of them. The poison is called *ricin* and is considered to be a blood poison. It is soluble in water so can be easily removed from the oil that is extracted from the seeds and used in medicine. Especially fortunate for me is the fact that soaking the beans in water removes the poisonous material. Not knowing that castor beans were poisonous I once ate nearly a dozen with the result that I was very ill. If the beans had not previously been soaked in water, I would never have lived to tell about it.

Note the unusual markings on castor beans.

COCKLEBUR

Among the common weed plants of waste places is the cockle-bur (*Xanthium*), a plant with an erect stem and heart-shaped leaves. The blooms are inconspicuous but in late summer the seed pods are formed, each containing two seeds. The pods themselves are nearly an inch in length and completely covered with recurved spines that enable them to hook onto clothing or the fur of animals to secure transportation to distant places.

Within the leaves and young seeds is contained a poisonous glucoside called *Xanthostrumarim*. Livestock are often killed by eating the young leaves, but apparently the seeds are also harmful since pigs are sometimes killed by eating them. Some authorities believe, however, that it is usually the mechanical injury caused by the sharp spines on the seed pods rather than a toxin that harms animals.

BUCKEYE

There are several kinds of buckeye shrubs (*Aesculus*) found growing in many places. Some have red flowers while others have white flowers. The leaves are palmate or formed of from five to seven leaflets attached to a central point like the fingers of the hand. The fruit, which matures in late summer, consists of a leathery capsule containing from one to three large, brown

Cocklebur pods are covered with curved spines.

A buckeye pod cut open to show the seeds within

seeds. The plants get their name from the fancied resemblance of the seeds to buck eyes, but sometimes the plants are also called horse chestnuts.

Both the leaves and the nuts are considered to be quite poisonous and have killed children who ate them. The young shoots seem to be especially poisonous. Buckeye poison affects the nervous system, causing dizziness, staggering, and eye dilation.

FLAX

Flax has long been cultivated in many countries, especially for its fiber which is woven into linen. As a matter of fact, the use of flax fiber for weaving goes back to prehistoric times. It has been found among the remains of the ancient Swiss Lake Dwellers and was also cultivated by the ancient Egyptians.

In addition to the fiber from the stems, a valuable oil is obtained from the seeds and what remains after the oil is extracted is pressed into linseed cake, an important stock food. Linseed oil, of course, is used in paint and varnish. Occasionally, livestock are killed by eating the cake, since the seeds contain a glucoside called *phaseolunatin,* a poisonous substance that also occurs in certain beans.

The larkspurs (*Delphinium*) are low, flowering plants, various kinds of which are found in nearly all parts of the country. They bear characteristic blooms, usually deep blue or purple, though some kinds have white flowers. The leaves are of palmate form. Wild larkspurs are common on the western prairies and in other places, but some kinds are grown in flower gardens. Larkspurs have been known for many centuries. Indeed, Pliny, the ancient writer and naturalist, stated that the powdered seeds were effective in destroying head lice and the plants were also used in medicine.

To western ranchers the larkspurs are anything but attractive prairie flowers since cattle are often killed by eating them. Most losses of livestock occur when the young plants are eaten in early spring, but cattle are also killed later in the season. The poisonous alkaloids in larkspurs are *delphinine, delphinoidine, delphisine* and *staphisagroine*. The first of these is the most poisonous. These poisons are especially abundant in the seeds.

MUSTARD

Many plants, while not ordinarily considered to be poisonous, do sometimes cause illness when eaten. Plants of the mustard family are good examples. Many of our most popular vegetables belong to this large family and contain no toxic substances. Radishes, broccoli, cauliflower and cabbage are common examples. But the seeds of some wild mustards contain poisonous materials that can cause illness. Many mustard seeds contain glucosides which, when acted upon by enzymes, liberate mustard oil which is irritating to the animal digestive system. Because of these irritating properties, powdered white mustard is often used in medicine as a strong emetic and stimulant.

Horse-radish, a member of the mustard family, contains strong irritants also. While it can be eaten or used as a seasoning in small quantities, it may be harmful in large amounts.

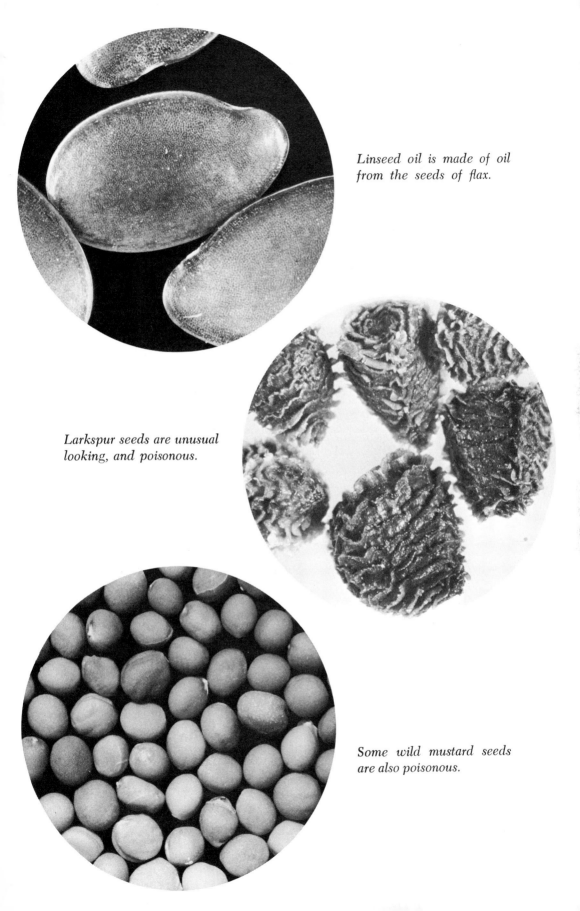

Linseed oil is made of oil from the seeds of flax.

Larkspur seeds are unusual looking, and poisonous.

Some wild mustard seeds are also poisonous.

CROTALARIA

Rattlebox plants (*Crotalaria*) bear relatively large, pealike pods within which are contained many shiny seeds. These have a very characteristic shape. When the pods are dry the seeds break loose from their points of attachment and rattle about inside, making a noise like a rattlesnake when the plant is shaken. Whether or not this sound serves any useful purpose seems doubtful, but it is from this noise-making characteristic that the plant got its name.

Most of the various kinds of rattlebox plants occur in the Tropice but there are several that are common in the United States. They are small plants with yellow flowers of pealike form that appear from June to September. The pods, when mature, are from one to two inches long.

Poisonous alkaloids are found in all parts of the plants, especially in the seeds, and horses and other livestock are often killed. Such poisoning seems to be especially common in the Midwest along the sandy beds of the Missouri River. For this reason, livestock poisoning by *Crotalaria* is often called "Missouri bottom disease."

LUPINE-THE-WOLF

Lupines of various kinds are found growing wild in many parts of the country, especially in the West where they are a characteristic part of the vegetation of the sagebrush prairies. Showy kinds are often grown in flower gardens for their blooms. The state flower of Texas, the bluebonnet, is a lupine. Lupines are low herbs with downy, palmate leaves and dark blue, pealike flowers. Indeed, they belong to the legume or pea family. In ancient times, they were called wolfplants since it was believed that they consumed all the nourishment from the soil. The name "lupine" comes from the Latin name for wolf, *lupus.*

Fortunately, not all kinds of lupines are poisonous, but the poisonous kinds are quite difficult to tell from those that are not. The poisons contained in these plants are *lupinine, lupanine,*

Seeds rattling about inside the dry pods give Crotalaria *its more common name of rattlebox plant.*

Poisonous lupine seeds annually cause the loss of many cattle and sheep on western ranges.

sparteine and other alkaloids, but not all lupines contain the same poisons. While all parts of some lupines are poisonous when eaten, the toxic substances seem to be concentrated in the mature seeds. Since livestock on the western ranges often feed upon the plants, many animals are often killed. As a matter of fact, the disease caused by eating the plant is called *lupinosus* and is responsible for the loss of more cattle and sheep than any other poisonous range plant.

Close-up of Physalis *fruit which contains the berry*

Cut-away of Physalis *fruit showing the enclosed berry*

Greatly enlarged seeds of Physalis, *a nightshade*

CHAPTER 8

Seeds and Their Pods

S eed pods are just as varied as the seeds they contain. To a botanist, a pod is a dry fruit which becomes hard and leathery at maturity. Most pods, when mature, split open along definite seams to liberate their seeds. Peas and beans split along each side of the pod and the two parts then separate. Pods of larkspur and columbine have several seed-bearing sections which split open along only one side. A somewhat different arrangement is found in lily, snapdragon, tulip, and evening primrose. In the case of these flowers the seed containers are called *capsules* and are made up of two or more seed-bearing sections fused together. In the members of the mustard family, to which shepherd's-purse and pennycress belong, the seed containers are called *siliques* and, at maturity, the two halves separate, leaving thin partitions between them.

PHYSALIS

Physalis, often found growing as a weed in abandoned places, is sometimes called ground cherry. It is a member of the nightshade family and the Greek name, *Physalis,* means "bladder." The small, tomato-like fruit is enclosed with a thin protective envelope shaped like a Japanese lantern. Some kinds of these plants are quite ornamental and are grown in gardens. The wild species is probably not poisonous, but the fruit should not be eaten since some nightshades are very poisonous.

123

Seed pod of althea

Althea seeds

ALTHEA

Althea is a flowering shrub belonging to the mallow family. The seeds, which are contained in five-parted pods, have fringing hairs which may aid in their dispersal. Cotton also belongs to the mallow family. Diameter of pod: ½ inch. Diameter of seed: ¼ inch.

Pods of pennycress

Pennycress seeds

PENNYCRESS

Pennycress or Frenchweed is a common weed in portions of northern United States. A native of Europe and Asia, it probably came to this country on ship ballast. It belongs to the mustard family and bears small, white flowers. The seed pods are flat and the seeds, which are quite small, have distinctive markings.

Skullcap seed pods

Skullcap seeds

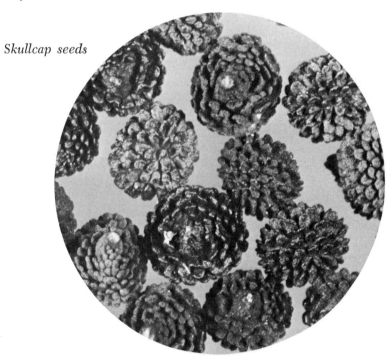

SKULLCAP

Skullcap (*Scutellaria*) belongs to the mint family and receives its name from the strange form of its seed pods. Its blooms are quite attractive, resembling miniature snapdragons, and the seeds are very characteristic in form and easily identified.

Seed pods of bull-horn acacia

BULL-HORN ACACIA

The bull-horn acacias grow in the American Tropics. They are shrubs or small trees armed with long thorns resembling the horns of Texas longhorns. Vicious ants live within the hollow thorns and protect the plants. The seeds resemble those of mimosa and other closely related members of the legume family. Length of pod: 3 inches.

Bull-horn acacia seeds

Dry pod of rattlebox plant, showing loose seeds that rattle

RATTLEBOX

Rattlebox (*Crotalaria*) belongs to the pea family. The attractive flowers are yellow and pealike. When the pods are mature and dry the shiny seeds break loose and rattle about inside. When the dry plant with many attached pods is shaken it makes a sound like an angry rattlesnake. Length of pod: 1 inch.

Green pod of rattlebox, cut open to show developing seeds

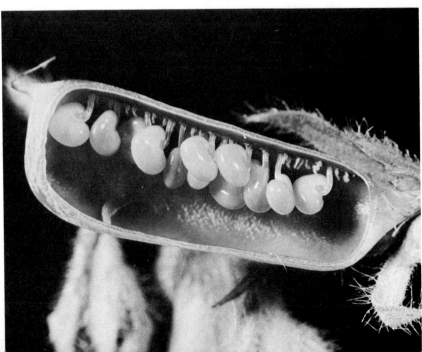

Bloom of white campion

White campion seeds

WHITE CAMPION

This pretty white flower grows in waste places. It is closely related to catchfly, corn cockle and pink. The seeds of all these flowers are similar in form and appearance and are easily identified. They are enclosed in thin pods at the base of the flower.

Leaves and winged seed pods of wild yam-root

Both the pods and seeds of wild yam-root are winged.

WILD YAM-ROOT

This is a climbing vine with attractive, heart-shaped leaves that is usually found in deep forests. Its flowers are pale greenish-yellow and the seed pods bear three wings like the begonia. Within these angular pods are winged seeds. The botanical name is *Dioscoria*, from the Greek naturalist, Dioscorides. Diameter of pod: ¾ inch. Diameter of seed: ⅜ inch.

130

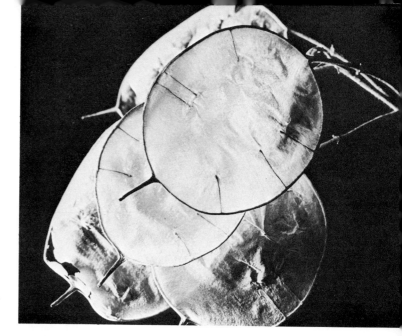

Decorative pods of honesty plant, or moonwort

Seeds of the honesty plant are flat and rounded.

HONESTY PLANT

This unusual plant bears circular, moon-shaped seed pods which account for its scientific name *Lunaria* (*luna* is the Latin name for moon). It is also called moonwort. The one-inch wide seed pods are thin and silvery and, since the seeds can be seen through their walls, they are called honesty plants. The pods here have no seeds. Dry pods are used in flower arrangements.

131

Honey locust tree with pods

HONEY LOCUST

This is a common tree of eastern United States. It bears vicious thorns on both the twigs and the trunk. It is a legume and thus its seed pods, which may reach a foot in length, are pealike and hang suspended from the twigs. The seeds resemble beans. Length of pod: 8 inches.

Seeds of honey locust

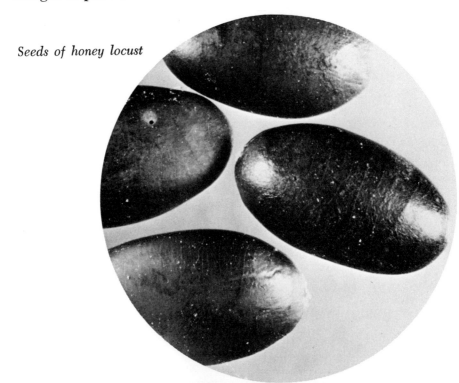

Catalpa tree with seed pods

CATALPA

The catalpa or Indian bean is an attractive, spreading tree native to the United States. In spring it bears bell-shaped flowers and the fruit, when mature, is a long, slender pod containing many seeds, each equipped with two long, pointed wings. Length of pod: 6 inches.

Winged catalpa seeds

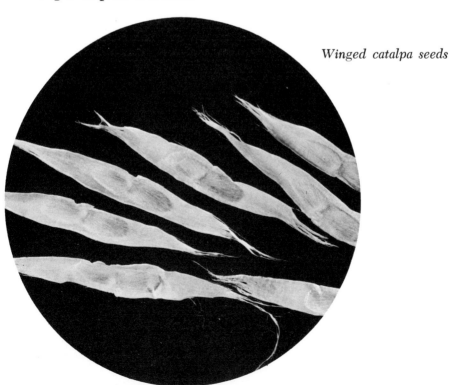

Spurge nettle pod, with the spines clearly visible

SPURGE NETTLE

Spurge nettle (*Jatropha stimulosa*) is also called tread-softly, a name that is very apt since treading on one of these plants with bare feet could be very unpleasant indeed. The entire plant, including the seed pods, is covered with needle-like spines containing an irritating substance that causes intense itching on contact with the skin. It belongs to the castor bean family. Diameter of pod: ½ inch.

Spurge nettle seeds

Cleome, the spiderflower,
with pods at top of stalk

CLEOME

This ornamental flower is often grown in flower gardens for its attractive blooms that rapidly open at dusk at almost exactly the same time each evening. There are a number of tropical species, but smaller, native species occur in the United States where they are called bee plants or spiderflowers. Cleome blooms over a long period with new flowers opening at the top of the stalk as the three-inch seed pods mature progressively upward.

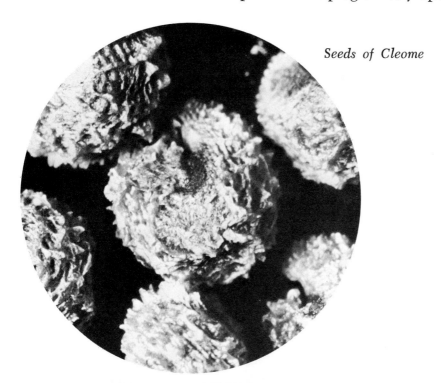

Seeds of Cleome

Seeds of the Chinese varnish tree can be seen within the split follicles.

PARASOL TREE

Shown here is the mature fruit of the parasol tree (*Sterculia*), also called Japanese or Chinese varnish tree. This tree, a native of China and Japan, is often grown in southern United States. At maturity the follicles containing the seeds split into four sections to which the seeds are attached.

Two dodder seed pods and dodder seeds

Shepherd's-purse plant   *Seeds of shepherd's-purse*

DODDER

Dodder is a strange parasitic little vine that attaches itself to other plants and sucks out their nourishment. Sometimes clover is seriously damaged. When a dodder seed germinates on the ground it sends out a slender stem which twines about until it touches a plant to which it rapidly attaches itself. Shown here are two dodder pods and some seeds.

SHEPHERD'S-PURSE

This is one of our best-known weeds and its botanical name, *Capsella bursa-pastoris,* is quite descriptive. *Capsella* means "little box" which describes the triangular seed pods; *bursa* means "sac" and *pastoris* is "shepherd." The plant has small, white flowers and belongs to the mustard family. Diameter of pod: ⅛ inch.

137

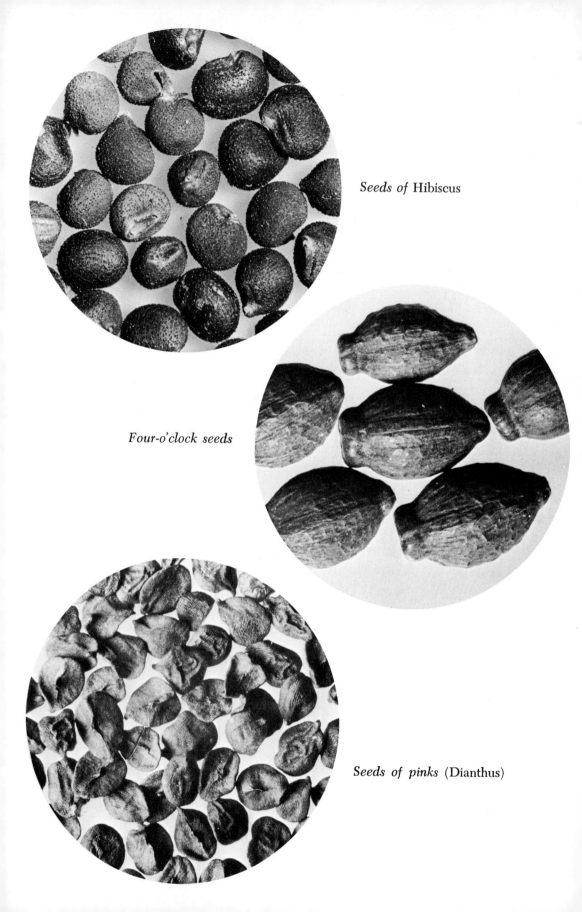

Seeds of Hibiscus

Four-o'clock seeds

Seeds of pinks (Dianthus)

CHAPTER 9

Seeds of the Flower and Herb Garden

The growing of flowers is an ancient craft and many of our common garden flowers and herbs had their origins in far lands of long ago. The seeds in the colorful packets we buy today are the result of careful breeding over the years. They come in astonishing shapes, colors and sizes, and within each seed is the blueprint of a plant. Here are some of those seeds, magnified and photographed to show their interesting details.

HIBISCUS

Hibiscus flowers are among our most showy kinds, but they are especially common in tropical countries. Various kinds are found in China, Africa and other places. The seeds are spherical and of rather small size since there are about 4,000 to the ounce.

FOUR-O'CLOCK

The popular four-o'clock (*Mirabilis jalapa*) has large, gourd-shaped seeds that average only about 325 per ounce. It thrives as far north as New York, but is a native of Tropical America from which it gets its other common name, "marvel of Peru."

PINK

Pinks or carnations (*Dianthus*) have always been favorites in flower gardens. There are many kinds found in many lands. The

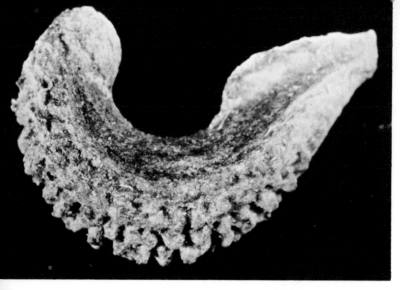

Seeds of calendula have an odd shape.

seeds of the common garden pink are black in color with interesting surface markings. There are about 14,000 seeds per ounce so they may be regarded as being of small size.

CALENDULA

The seeds of calendula (*Calendula officinalis*), sometimes called pot marigold, are of unusual shape. They are relatively large size, with about 3,000 seeds per ounce. These common inhabitants of the flower garden have showy blooms and are native to Europe. In fact, calendula is the marigold of Shakespeare's time.

COCKSCOMB

There are a number of these flowers (*Celosia*) grown in gardens. Some have flower heads of crested form while others are in the form of graceful feathers or plumes. They belong to the pigweed family, and the seeds are small, since about 28,000 are required to weigh an ounce.

SUNFLOWER

The giant sunflower (*Helianthus*) often grows to a height of ten or more feet. The large flower heads are filled with seeds that

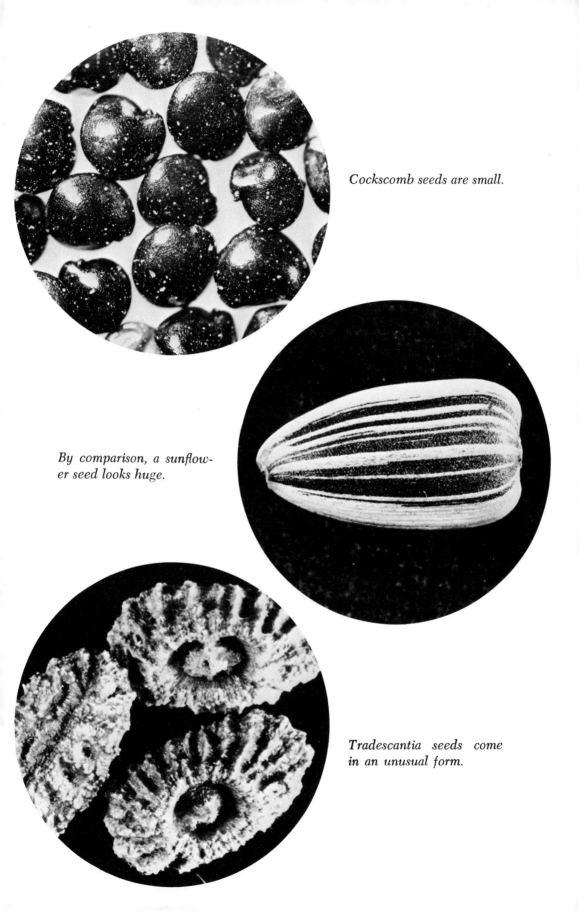

Cockscomb seeds are small.

By comparison, a sunflower seed looks huge.

Tradescantia seeds come in an unusual form.

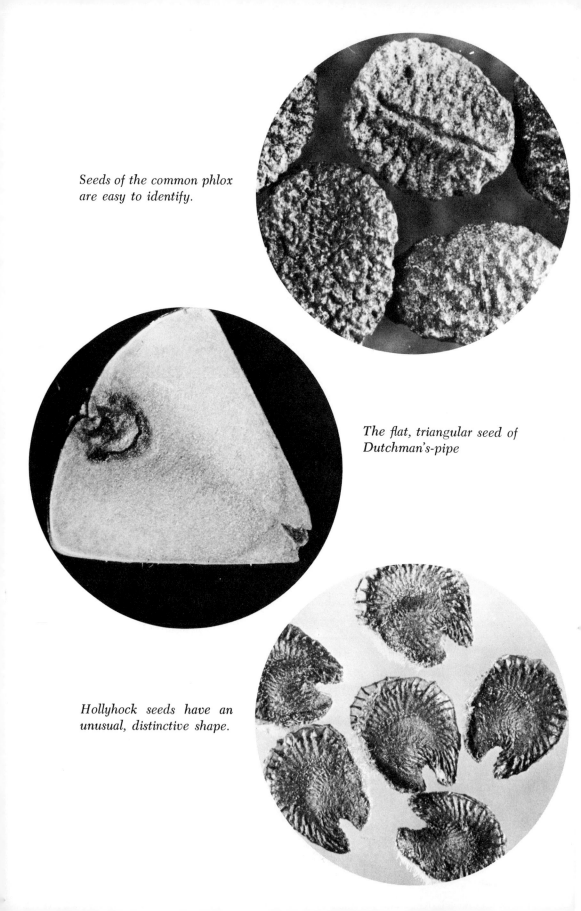

Seeds of the common phlox are easy to identify.

The flat, triangular seed of Dutchman's-pipe

Hollyhock seeds have an unusual, distinctive shape.

are excellent for feeding wild birds in winter. Due to their large size there are only 650 seeds to the ounce.

TRADESCANTIA

These flowers, often called spiderworts, are perennials grown in many gardens. Some grow erect while others are trailing. Their flowers are usually blue, but there are also kinds with red or white flowers. Some kinds grow wild. The seeds are of unusual form and very small.

PHLOX

In this case the common name is also the botanical name. It comes from the ancient Greek name meaning "flame." One kind of phlox is called sweet William, and gilias belong to the same family. Phlox seeds are of characteristic form and easily identified. There are about 14,000 to the ounce.

DUTCHMAN's-PIPE

These flowers (*Aristolochia*) are climbing vines with unusual blooms shaped like curved pipes. The rear portion of the flower is expanded into a chamber within which small flies are trapped for pollination. The seeds are flat and of triangular shape.

A cornflower seed, greatly magnified as are the other seeds in this book

These tiny shuttlecocks are seeds of Scabiosa.

HOLLYHOCK

Hollyhocks (*Althaea*) have been cultivated in flower gardens for centuries. Their blooms are many colors and their seeds of characteristic shape. There are about 3,000 seeds to the ounce.

CORNFLOWER

The attractive cornflowers (*Centaurea*) are also known by other names such as centaury and bachelor's button. They belong to the daisy family and there are many kinds or species. The unusual seeds may be considered of moderate size since there are about 7,000 to the ounce.

SCABIOSA

These flowers received their Latin name from the fact that they were once used in medicine. The name means "itch." There are several kinds, all native to Europe and Asia. The seeds look like tiny shuttlecocks.

SNAPDRAGON

Snapdragons (*Antirrhinum*) are one of our most attractive garden flowers. Their blooms are of characteristic shape, re-

144

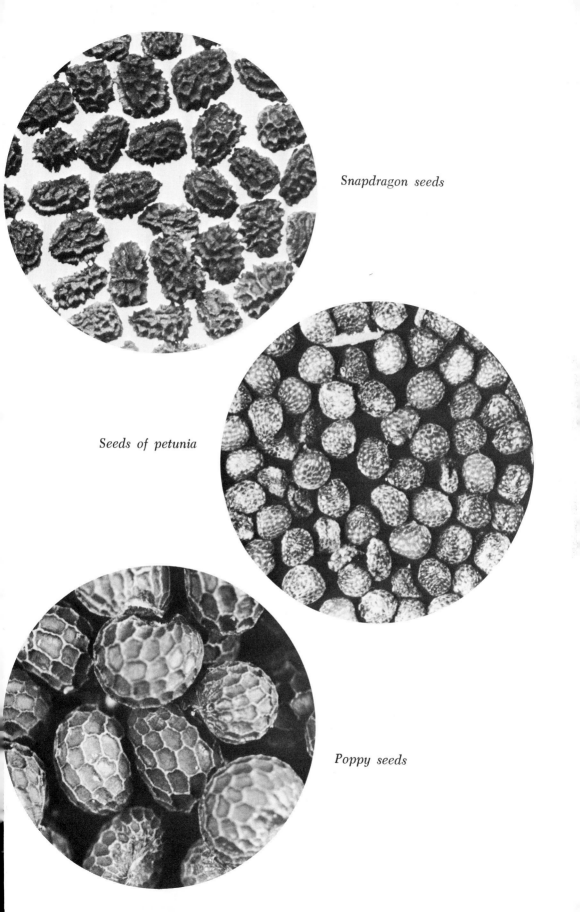

Snapdragon seeds

Seeds of petunia

Poppy seeds

Poppy seeds are used in cooking and their oil has valuable commercial uses. Compare these seeds with the enlarged poppy seeds on page 145.

sembling the fanciful heads of dragons. The botanical name means "shaped like a nose." There are 125,000 seeds to the ounce.

PETUNIA

Like phlox, the common name of these common flowers is also their botanical name. They belong to the tobacco family. Petunia seeds are very small, there being 285,000 to the ounce.

POPPY

Poppies are of numerous kinds and colors, many of which have been bred by horticulturists. The common garden variety is the Oriental poppy (*Papaver orientale*). Poppies have had a long history stretching back into the gardens of ancient Persia. The seeds are easily identified; there are about 140,000 to the ounce. Poppy seed is sold for use in cooking; it is sprinkled on rolls, cookies, and used with noodles and other foods.

CARAWAY

Caraway seeds are produced by the caraway plant (*Carum carvi*), a member of the carrot family. It grows from one to two feet tall and bears small white flowers in a head. Sometimes the plants escape from cultivation and grow wild. Caraway seed is much used in flavoring bread, cakes and cheese. Sometimes the young plants are eaten.

Caraway seeds are often added to rye bread.

DILL

The seeds of dill (*Anethum graveolens*) are much used in seasoning cheese spread, stews, pickles and sauerkraut. The plant is a member of the parsley family (*Umbelliferae*) which also includes sweet cicely, poison hemlock, caraway, and carrot. Dill plants grow about three feet tall and bear small, yellow flowers. Medicinal preparations were once made from the leaves. It is a native of Europe.

Seeds of the dill plant

Seeds almost seem to have "wills to survive." Here a pine seedling grows up out of a small hollow in a stump where the seed had lodged. The surrounding forest has been burned.

One of the first plants to come up after forest fires is the fireweed (Epilobium). It is a tall plant with attractive pink blooms.

CHAPTER 10

Some Seeds of Field and Forest

Forest fires are enemies of wild flowers, trees, and wildlife. Many trees such as the Sequoias have very thick bark and so can withstand the heat of great fires, but their seeds are usually destroyed. The plants best able to survive fires are the weeds and some wild flowers, because some of their seeds are apt to be hidden in the soil. Some seeds survive fires better than others; the first flowers to appear in burned-over areas of western forests are willow herbs or fireweeds (*Epilobium angustifolium*). The stems of these plants reach up to seven feet, at the tops of which are clusters of pretty pink blooms. Early settlers used the leaves as a substitute for tea. Fireweeds of other kinds occur in eastern United States.

As stated earlier, the seeds of many plants may remain alive in the soil for many years, germinating when conditions are finally right. Seeds have amazing abilities to survive. Nature has been slowly fitting them for survival for millions of years, so in spite of fires and other natural catastrophes, plants, through their seeds, will continue to clothe the earth. In many cases, fires are actually helpful to some plants since larger plants that shade them out are removed, allowing them to grow.

If you walk through fields and forests in the late autumn you will find that many plants and trees are shedding their seeds. Frosts have killed most of the smaller plants but their seeds will survive the winter. Let's consider a few of these wild seeds.

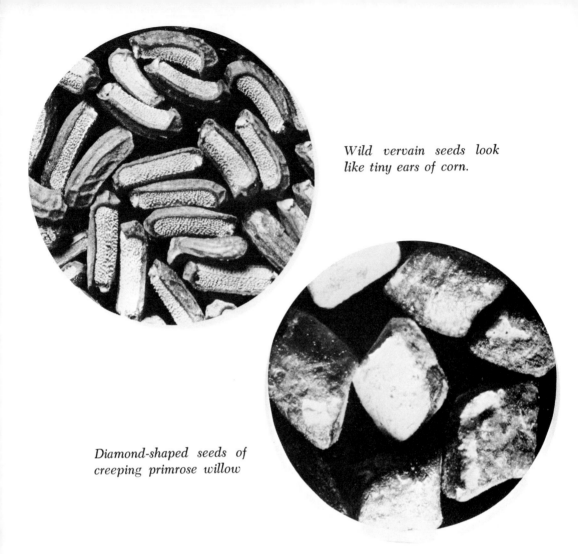

Wild vervain seeds look like tiny ears of corn.

Diamond-shaped seeds of creeping primrose willow

VERVAIN

The vervains (*Verbena*) have seeds of unusual form. Shown here are seeds of a wild vervain, but the seeds of cultivated species are similar.

CREEPING PRIMROSE-WILLOW

The seeds of this plant (*Jussiaea*) have an unusual diamond shape. Primrose-willows grow in or near water and have flowers with four yellow petals. The seeds are probably distributed by water birds.

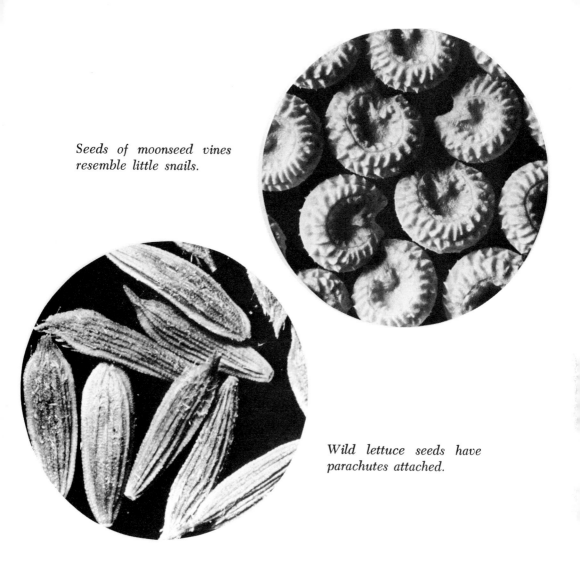

Seeds of moonseed vines
resemble little snails.

Wild lettuce seeds have
parachutes attached.

MOONSEED

These interesting seeds are produced by a little vine found in woodland thickets. In autumn, clusters of red berries appear which contain the unusual seeds. Since the seeds resemble tiny snails, the vine is sometimes called "snail-seed vine."

WILD LETTUCE

Wild lettuce (*Lactuca*) is closely related to our common garden lettuce, but it grows as a tall weed and is not edible. The seeds have parachutes like those of dandelion.

151

Seeds of Maypop are contained in a fleshy fruit.

Seeds of trailing arbutus, one of the heath family

MAYPOP

The blooms of the Maypop (*Passiflora*) are among our loveliest kinds. They are about three inches in diameter, and consist of a ring of purple and white fringelike filaments instead of broad petals. The fruit is large, fleshy and contains many seeds.

TRAILING ARBUTUS

This plant (*Epigaea*) is a creeping member of the heath family that produces rose-colored flowers in early spring. They are quite pretty and have a spicy fragrance. The plant is common on the slopes of the eastern mountains.

SWEET CICELY

This plant (*Osmorhiza*) belongs to the parsley family and bears small, white flowers. The twin, barbed seeds are attached to the tips of the branching stems. Note their unusual means of attachment.

COASTAL REDWOOD

The coastal redwood (*Sequoia sempervirens*) may grow to 350 feet tall, but these trees do not grow as large in diameter or as old as the Big Tree Sequoias of the mountains. They begin producing seeds when about 20 years old. The seeds of both kinds of Sequoias are only about a quarter of an inch long and are shed in autumn.

BIG TREE SEQUOIA

The seeds of the Big Tree (*Sequoia gigantea*) are very small compared to the size of the trees that produce them. These great trees may grow to 35 feet in diameter at the base and live to be several thousand years old. They do not begin producing seeds until they are about 125 years of age.

The twin seeds of sweet cicely have barbs at the tips. It is a plant in the parsley family.

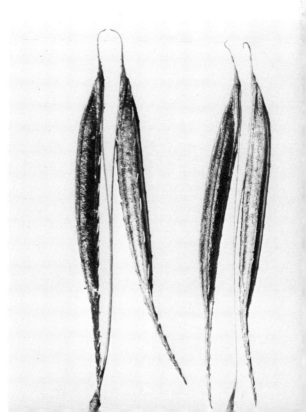

Seeds of coastal redwood

Big Tree Sequoia seeds

COLLECTING WILD FLOWER SEEDS

The collection and study of wild flower seeds can be an interesting hobby. They are among the most beautiful small objects in nature. Their forms are of endless variety and many kinds are quite colorful. Unusual surface markings help in identification.

Very little equipment is required for this fascinating hobby.

154

Only a few items are necessary for collecting wild flower and other plant seeds: graduated sieves, tweezers, hand lens, and vials for storage. For field collecting, a supply of coin envelopes (not shown) is excellent.

The first thing needed is a good manual by which the plants can be identified. There are several seed identification manuals available. Beyond this, you should have a supply of envelopes and vials. The envelopes are used for field collecting, while the vials are for final storage of individual batches of seeds. Labels should, of course, be attached giving all necessary data, including scientific names. In the handling of flower seeds, a pair of sharp pointed tweezers is handy, as is a good hand lens of about 10-power.

Many state and government organizations have extensive seed collections. At the Patuxent Wildlife Research Center at Laurel, Maryland, there is a collection of more than 7,500 species. The Wild Flower Preservation Society in Washington, D.C., has a collection of about 5,000 species of seeds.

Index

Page numbers in **boldface** *are those on which illustrations appear.*

157

158

The Author

Entomologist Ross E. Hutchins is also an expert nature photographer, and this combination of interests has resulted in almost thirty years of studying, photographing and writing about insects, plants, animals and birds. Born in Montana, he grew up on a cattle ranch near Yellowstone Park. At Montana State College he majored in biological sciences and later he received his Ph. D. in zoology and entomology from Iowa State College.

Dr. Hutchins' articles and pictures of natural history subjects have appeared in encyclopedias, books and magazines, among them *National Geographic*, *Life* and *Natural History*, as well as such European publications as *Sie und Er*, *La Vie des Bêtes* and *Sciences et Avenir*. His books in the juvenile field include INSECT BUILDERS AND CRAFTSMEN; INSECTS—HUNTERS AND TRAPPERS; STRANGE PLANTS AND THEIR WAYS; WILD WAYS. His THIS IS A LEAF, THIS IS A FLOWER and THIS IS A TREE are companion volumes noted for their remarkable close-up photographs by the author.

Ross Hutchins lives in Mississippi where he is Director of the State Plant Board of Mississippi and Professor of Entomology at Mississippi State University.

DATE DUE		
OCT 10		
MAR 11 '81		
DEC 10		
		ALESCO